Introduction

The Science Coordination Group was set up with the aim of producing specialised revision material for National Curriculum Science.
This is one of a set of six Workbooks which provide a full course of tailor-made questions ideally suited to all the main Exam Board syllabuses for *GCSE Double Science*.

These Workbooks have been produced to complement the popular range of Revision Guides produced by the Science Coordination Group for GCSE Double Science.

Throughout these books there is constant emphasis on the inescapable need to ***keep learning the basic facts***. This simple message is hammered home without compromise and without remorse, and whilst this traditionally brutal philosophy may not be quite in line with some other approaches to education, we still rather like it. But only because it works.

	Quantity	Symbol	Standard Units	Formula
1	Potential Difference	V	volt, V	$V = I \times R$
2	Current	I	ampere, A	$I = V / R$
3	Resistance	R	ohm, Ω	$R = V / I$
4	Charge	Q	coulomb, C	$Q = I \times t$
5	Power	P	watt, W	$P = V \times I$ or $P = I^2R$
6	Energy	E	joule, J	$E = QV$ or $V = E/Q$
7	Time	t	second, s	$E = P \times t$ or $E = IVt$
8	Force	F	newton, N	$F = ma$
9	Mass	m	kilogram, kg	
10	Weight (a force)	W	newton, N	$W = mg$
11	Density	D	kg per m^3, kg/m^3	$D = m/V$
12	Moment	M	newton-metre, Nm	$M = F \times r$
13	Velocity or Speed	v or s	metre/sec, m/s	$s = d/t$
14	Acceleration	a	metre/sec^2, m/s^2	$a = \Delta v/t$ or $a = F/m$
15	Pressure	P	pascal, Pa (N/m^2)	$P = F/A$
16	Area	A	$metre^2$, m^2	$P_1V_1 = P_2V_2$
17	Volume	V	$metre^3$, m^3	
18	Frequency	f	hertz, Hz	$f = 1/T$ (T=time period)
19	Wavelength (a distance)	λ or d	metre, m	$v = f \times \lambda$ (wave formula)
20	Work done	Wd	joule, J	$Wd = F \times d$
21	Potential Energy	PE	joule, J	$PE = m \times g \times h$
22	Kinetic Energy	KE	joule, J	$KE = \frac{1}{2}mv^2$

$$\text{Efficiency} = \frac{\text{Useful work output}}{\text{Total energy input}}$$

$$\frac{\text{Primary Coil Voltage}}{\text{Secondary Voltage}} = \frac{\text{No. of turns on Primary Coil}}{\text{No. of turns on Secondary}}$$

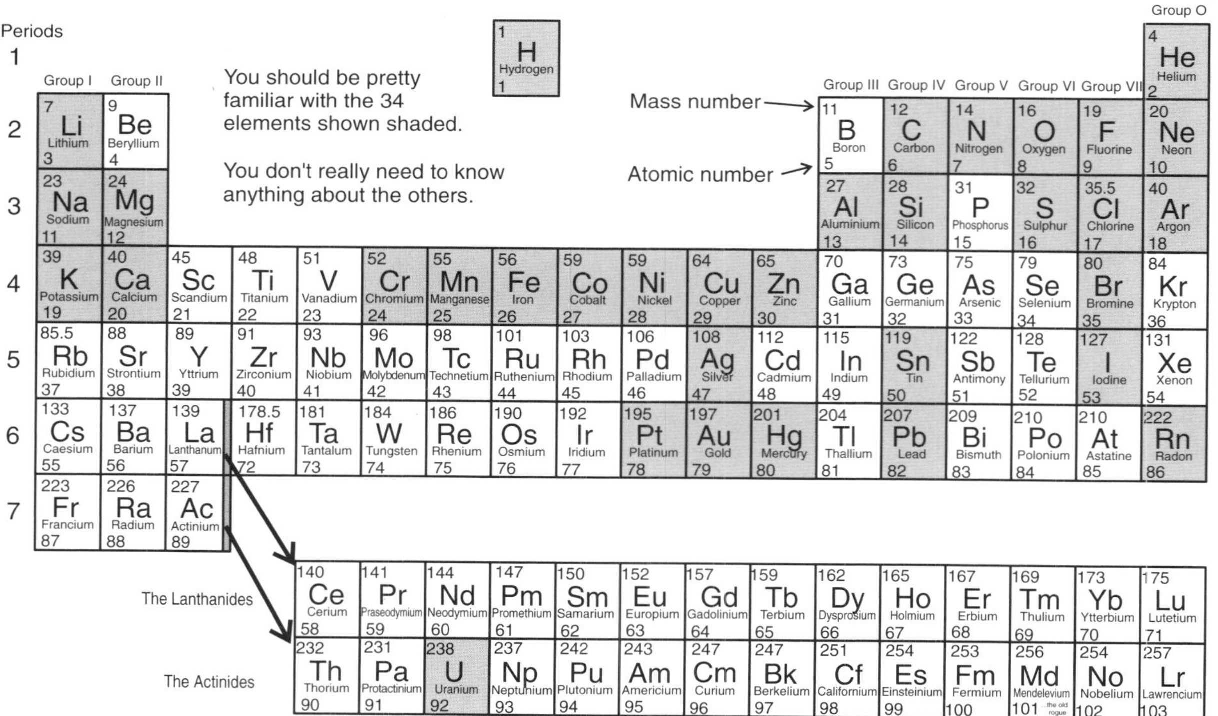

Contents

Published by Coordination Group Publications
Typesetting and layout by The Science Coordination Group
Illustrations by: Sandy Gardner, e-mail: zimkit@aol.com

Coordinated by Paddy Gannon BSc MA

Contributors
Bill Dolling
Jane Cartwright
Alex Kizildas

Printed by Hindson Print, Newcastle upon Tyne.

Questions on Common Physics Apparatus

Q1 Shown below are some pieces of equipment you will find in the laboratory. Write down the correct *name* for each one in the *space provided*.

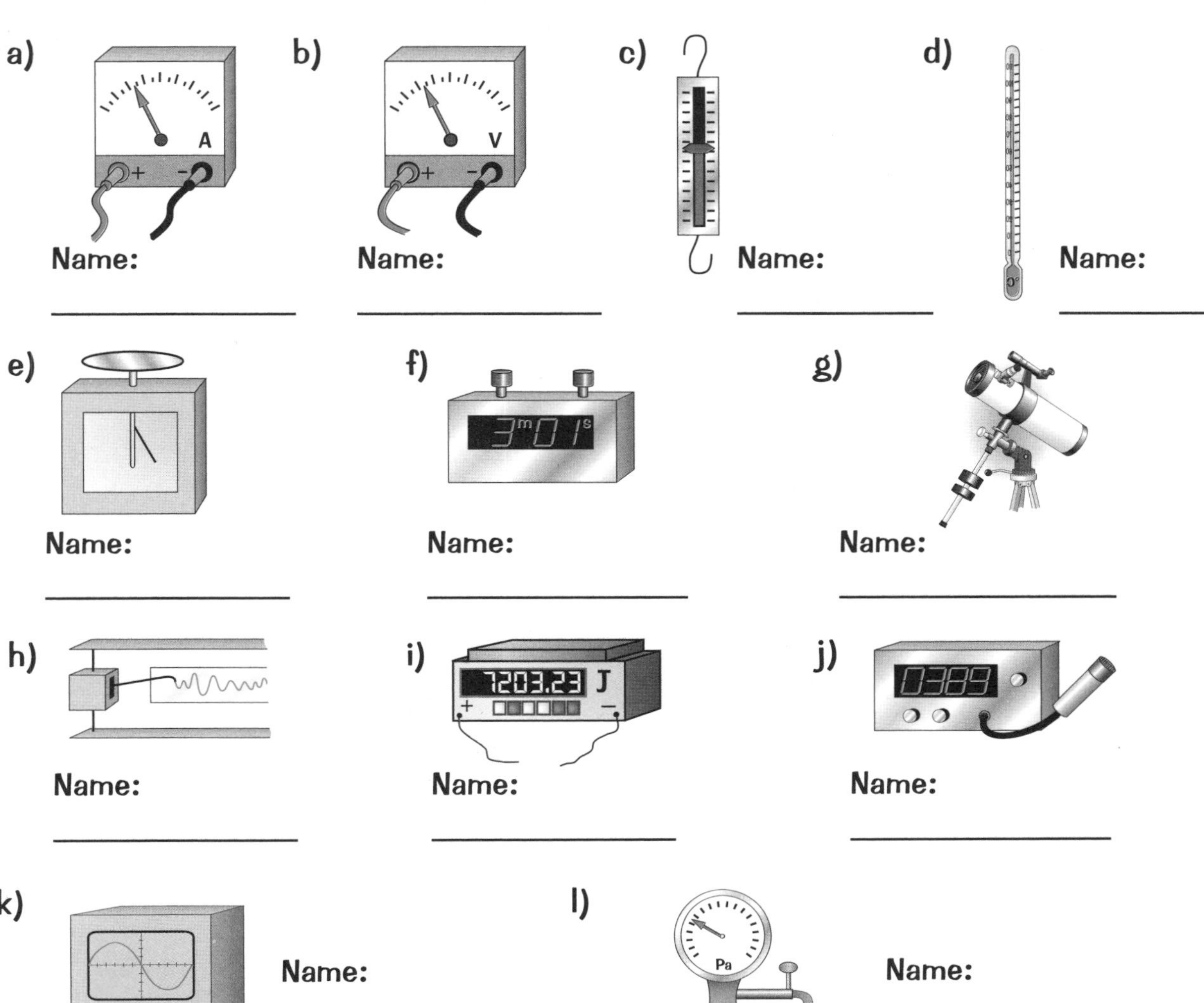

Q2 Which *piece of apparatus* shown above is used to:

a) measure *force?* ....

b) measure *radioactivity?* ....

c) measure the *current* in an electric circuit? ....

d) detect *electric charges?* ....

e) measure *time?* ....

f) measure *pressure?* ....

g) measure the amount of *electrical energy?* ....

h) display *electrical* signals? ....

i) detect and measure *seismic waves?* ....

j) *observe* the Universe? ....

k) measure *temperature?* ....

l) measure *voltage* difference? ....

Questions on Reading Scales

Q1 *A student carries out an experiment on electricity. An ammeter and voltmeter are used to measure the current through the resistor and the voltage across it.*

The meter reading taken in the experiment is shown opposite.

a) What *current* does the meter read? ....

b) What *voltage* does the meter read? ....

c) Use your answers to calculate the *resistance* of the resistor.

The equation that you need is:

$$\textbf{Resistance} = \frac{\textbf{Voltage}}{\textbf{Current}}$$

....

.... Answer ....

Q2 *Angela carries out an experiment to find the electrical energy used by a light bulb. She ran the experiment for 2 minutes.*

The reading on the joulemeter she used is shown opposite.

a) Write down the reading on the reading on the joulemeter and round it to the *nearest joule*.

....

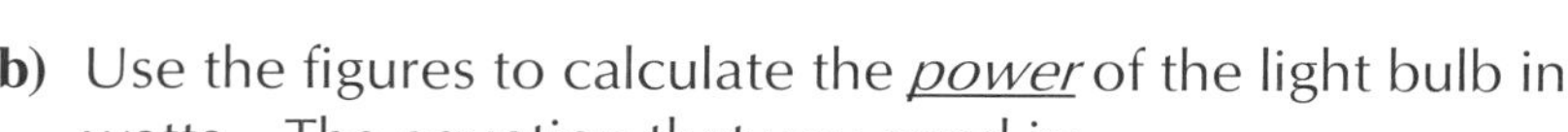

b) Use the figures to calculate the *power* of the light bulb in watts . The equation that you need is:

$$\textbf{P} = \frac{\textbf{E}}{\textbf{t}}$$

.... Answer ....

c) What should she do to be *more confident* of her result for the power of the light bulb?

....

Q3 *Neville is part of a group carrying out a radioactivity experiment. They take several readings of background radiation and the average count rate is found to be 14 counts/min.*

They place a detector near a radioactive source (which they know emits beta particles). The counter is switched on for 30 seconds and the reading on the counter is shown in the picture opposite.

a) Write down the *reading on the counter*. ....

b) Calculate the *count rate* in *counts per minute*. ....

c) What is the count rate (per min.) due to the *source* alone? ....

Questions on Reading Scales

Q4 *A group of students are carrying out an experiment on pressure and they use a Bourdon gauge for their measurements.*

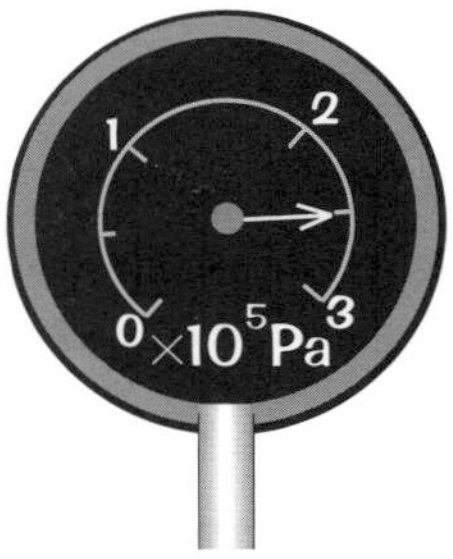

a) Write down the reading on the gauge shown opposite. Give your answer in *kilopascals* (kPa). ....

0 1 2 3 $\times 10^5$ Pa

b) They notice that when they disconnect the gauge from the apparatus, the arrow does not return to zero. *Why is this?* ....

....

Q5 *Abbie is using an old forcemeter to measure weights.*

Abbie looks at the scale of the forcemeter (shown opposite) before any weights have been hung on.

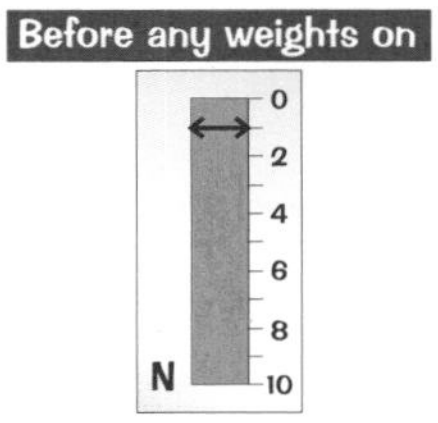

Before any weights on
0 2 4 6 8 10 N

Then the first weight is *attached...*

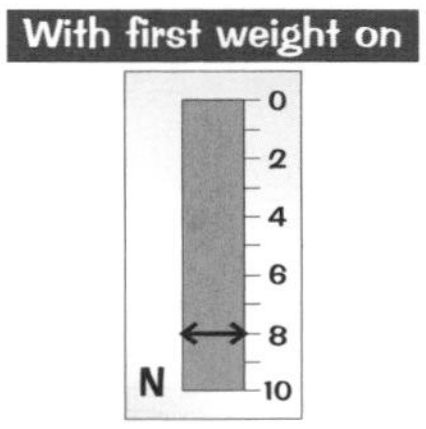

With first weight on
0 2 4 6 8 10 N

a) Look at the two scales above and *work out the force* pulling the weight downwards.

....

b) What *causes* this downward force? ....

c) How would the reading on the forcemeter be different if the weight was hung in a *beaker of water?* ....

Q6 The pictures below show some readings. Write down the *reading* and its *correct unit* in the spaces provided.

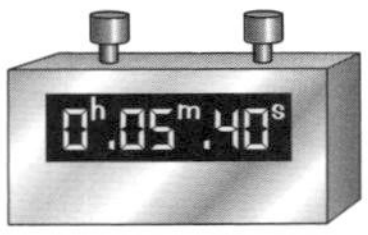

$0^h.05^m.40^s$

Reading __________

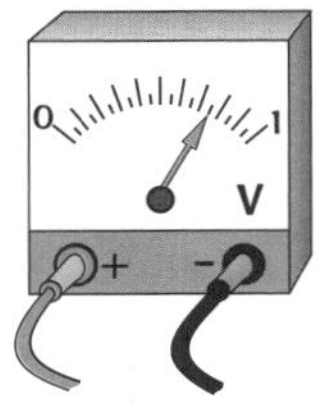

0 V 1

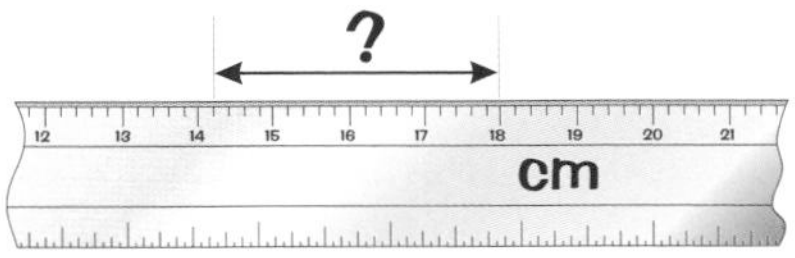

Reading __________

Reading __________

°C

0 Amps 8

Reading __________

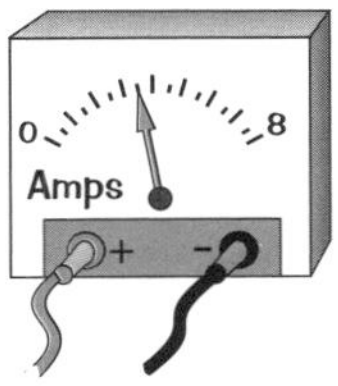

? 12 13 14 15 16 17 18 19 20 21 cm

Reading __________

N 0

Reading __________

Questions on Units

Q1 In the table below, write down the *standard unit* for each of the quantities.

Quantity	Potential Difference	Power	Force	Velocity	Frequency	Current
Standard Unit						

Q2 In the table below, write down the *quantity* for each of the standard units.

Standard Unit	ohm	joule	kilogram	pascal	coulomb	second
Quantity						

Q3 *Physics units can be combined with other units to give new units.*

For each of the questions below write down (without using the names in the question) a *name* for the unit we will get, if we:

a) multiply amps by ohms ....

b) multiply amps by seconds ....

c) multiply kilograms by metres/(sec)^2 ....

d) divide newtons by (metres)^2 ....

e) multiply hertz by metres ....

f) multiply pascals by (metres)^2 ....

g) divide volts by amps ....

h) multiply newtons by metres ....

i) multiply coulombs by volts ....

j) divide joules by seconds ....

Q4 *A derived unit is just a multiple or sub-multiple of a unit, and it can sometimes be written by adding a prefix before the unit.* In the following, calculate how many:

a) seconds in 1 minute ....

b) hours in 23 days ....

c) metres in 5 km ....

d) kilograms in 700g ....

e) newtons in 0.5 kilonewtons ....

f) watts in 2 MW ....

g) coulombs in 5 microcoulombs ....

h) milliohms in 1 ohm ....

i) milliseconds in 9 seconds ....

j) watts in 33 kilowatts ....

Q5 Go through your physics notes and make a list of as many different physics units as you can find.

....

....

....

Questions on Using Formulae

Q1 Some formula triangles are drawn below.

a) 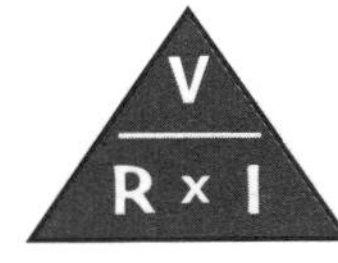

b) 

c) 

d) 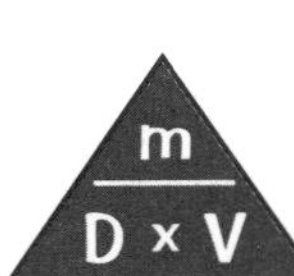

e) 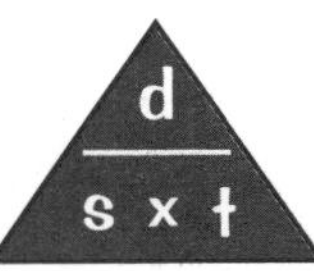

f) 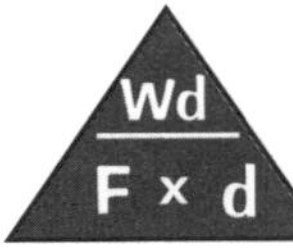

g) 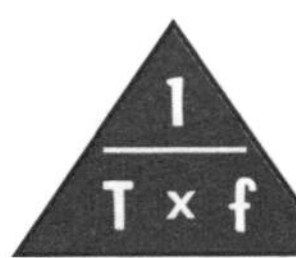

h) 

Choose which of the triangles (a) — (h) you would use to solve the following sums.

1. $I = \frac{Q}{t}$ .... 2. $d = s \times t$ .... 3. $V = I \times R$ .... 4. $P = \frac{E}{t}$ ....

5. **work done = force × distance** .... 6. **power = voltage × current** ....

7. **pressure = force ÷ area** .... 8. **frequency = 1 ÷ period** ....

Q2 In the following questions a) to d), write down the equation for the first quantity in terms of the other two quantities. The first one has been done for you.

a) R in terms of V and I,  R = **V / I**

b) t in terms of d and s, ⇒ t = ...

c) T in terms of f, ⇒ T = ...

d) V in terms of m and D,  V = ...

Q3 In the following questions, a) to d), write down the equation, *in words*, for the first quantity in terms of the other two quantities. Again, the first one has been done for you.

a) Charge in terms of current and time, ⇒ Charge = **Current × time**

b) Mass in terms of density and volume, ⇒ Mass = ...

c) Force in terms of work done and distance, ⇒ Force = ...

d) Current in terms of voltage and resistance, ⇒ Current = ...

Q4 It takes a mole 2.5 seconds to travel a distance of 8 metres down a tunnel.

What is the speed of the mole?

....

Speed of the mole is .... m/s

Questions on Current, Voltage, Resistance

Q1 Fill in the gaps in the following paragraph about electric current. Use the words in the grey box.

negative	circuit	charge	electrons	resistance	complete	voltage

Electric current is a flow of ______________ around a ______________. Electric current can only flow if there is a ______________ path from positive to ______________. The "push" behind the electricity is known as the potential difference or______________. Anything in the circuit will try to stop the current flowing through it. We call this the ______________.

In solid conductors, the electric charge is carried by a flow of ______________.

Q2 On the circuit diagram opposite, do the following:

a) Mark the positive side of the cell with a "+" sign.

b) Mark the negative side of the cell with a "–" sign.

c) Show the direction of the electric current with an arrow.

d) Label the resistor in the diagram with an "R".

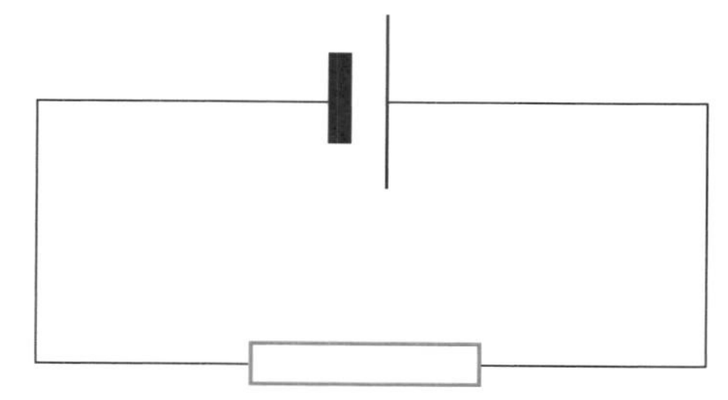

Q3 Complete the paragraph that follows by filling in the missing words. It is all about electrolysis.

ions	electrodes	liquid	water	melting	charged

Electrolysis is about passing electricity through a ______________. The right chemicals can be made into liquids by ______________ them or dissolving them in ______________. Only substances which contain electrically ______________ particles will pass electricity. The charged particles are called ______________. The particles in the liquid move towards the charged terminals called ______________.

When they get there, simpler substances are formed.

Q4 *The diagram opposite shows a liquid that is being used for electrolysis.*
– On the diagram,

a) Mark the positive electrode (+).

b) Mark the negative electrode (-).

c) Choose a positive ion and draw an arrow showing the direction it will move.

d) Choose a negative ion and draw an arrow showing the direction it will move.

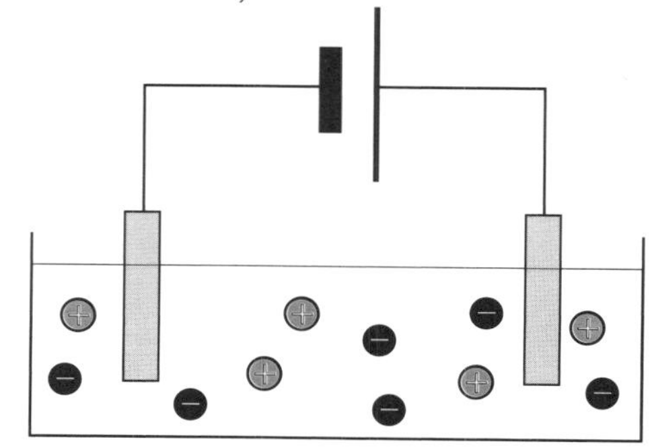

Questions on Current, Voltage, Resistance

Q5 For each part, circle the correct word in the brackets to complete the sentences.

a) *Electric current* is measured in (COULOMBS / AMPERES). Current is measured by a (AMMETER / JOULEMETER). This is always placed in (SERIES / PARALLEL) with the device.

b) *Potential difference* (or voltage) is measured in (VOLTS / JOULES). Potential difference is measured by a (FLOWMETER / VOLTMETER). This is always placed in (SERIES / PARALLEL) with the device.

Q6 Look at this diagram showing a voltmeter and an ammeter being used to measure electricity flowing through a bulb.

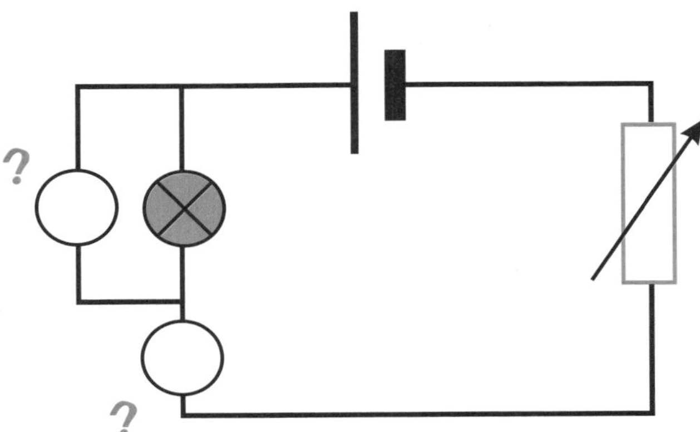

a) Label the ammeter with an "A".

b) Label the voltmeter with a "V".

c) Label the variable resistor.

d) Explain the purpose of the variable resistor in this circuit.

....

....

Q7 *When we measure current and voltage, different devices give different graphs.*

Drawn below are graphs of current plotted against voltage for the following three devices — *resistor*, *filament lamp* and *diode*.
For each graph, write down the correct device below it.

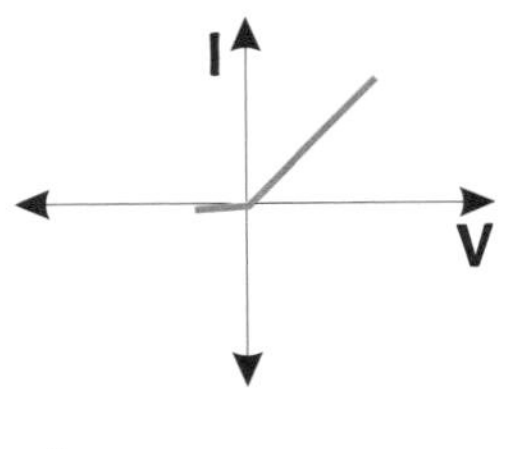

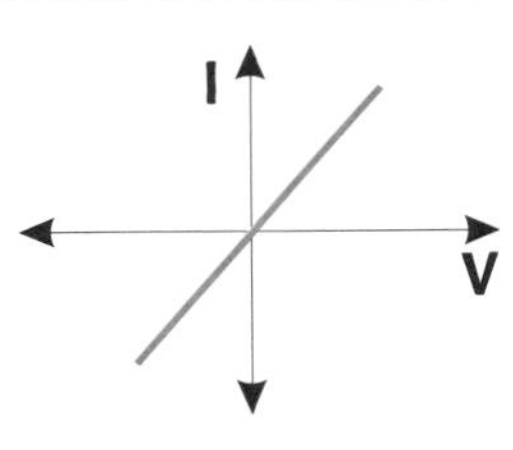

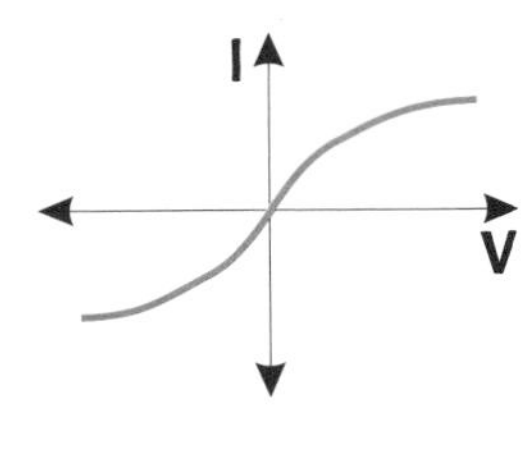

a) ____________ b) ____________ c) ____________

Q8 Here are 3 resistors. They all have the same resistance, but there are different voltages across them.

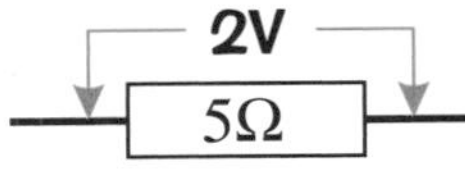

6V 5Ω

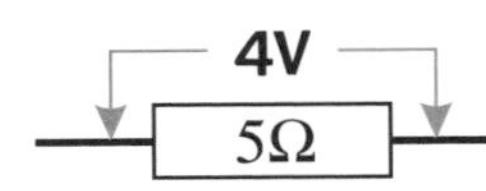

Just circle the one that will have the biggest current flowing through it.

Q9 Here are 3 more resistors. They are connected in turn to the same battery.

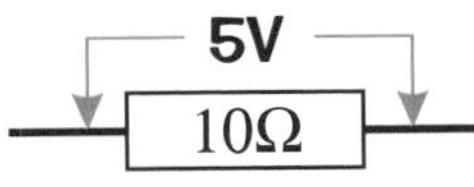

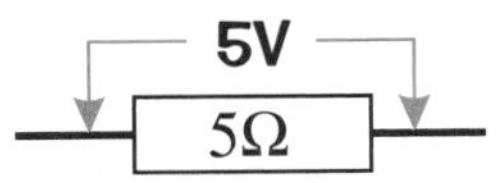

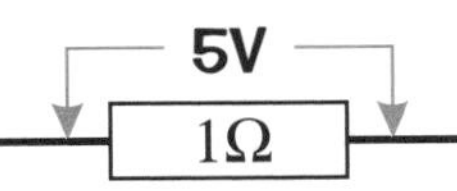

Just circle the one that will have the biggest current flowing through it.

Questions on Circuit Symbols and Devices

Q1 Look at the circuits, 1–6, that are drawn below. Try to work out what's in them, and then answer the questions that follow.

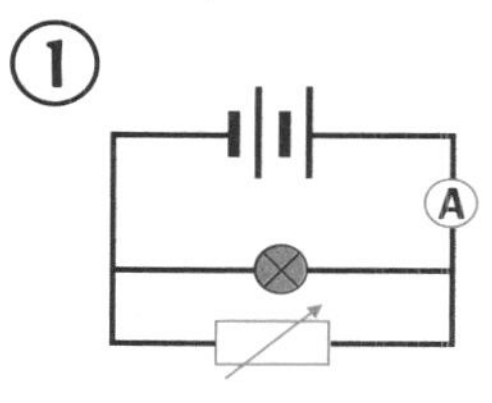

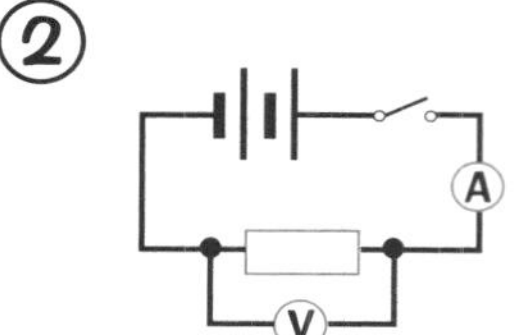

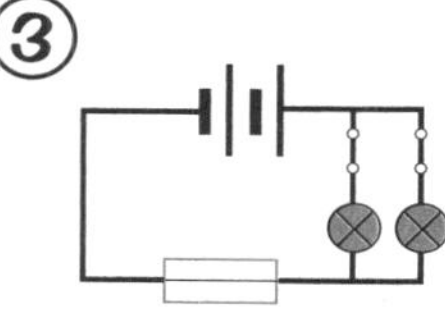

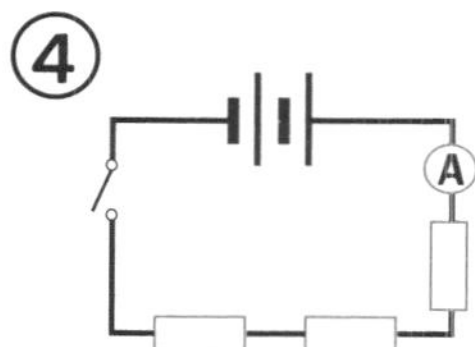

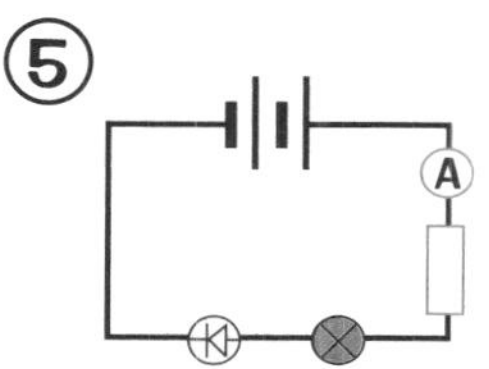

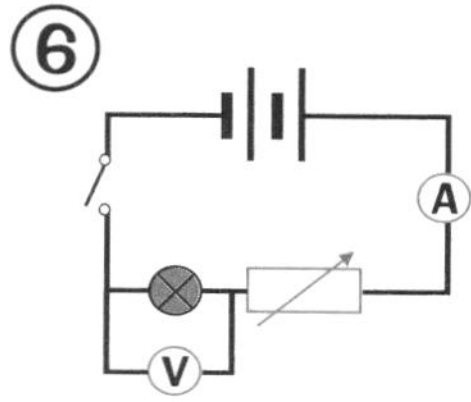

a) How many circuits contain filament lamps? 2 / 3 / 4

b) How many fixed resistors are there in circuit 4? 2 / 3 / 4

c) Which circuit contains a fuse? 3 / 5 / 6

d) What is the total number of switches? 2 / 4 / 5

e) How many of the switches are closed? 2 / 3 / 4

f) Which circuit contains a diode? 3 / 4 / 5

Q2 *You can use the following electrical components to change the brightness of a light.*

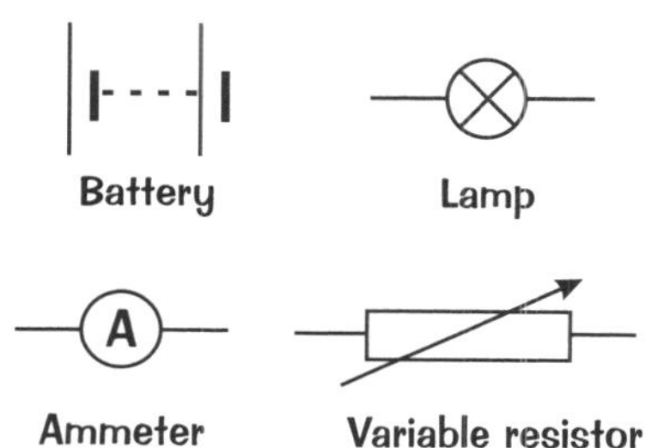

In the space opposite, draw a diagram of the circuit you would make to let you do this.

a) When the resistance of the resistor is increased, will the light get brighter or dimmer?

The variable resistor is replaced by 3 fixed resistors in turn. The values of these are 5 ohms, 10 ohms and 20 ohms.

b) Which resistor would give the dimmest light? ....

c) When electrical energy flows through the resistor, what sort of energy is produced?

....

Questions on Devices

Q1 *It is important you know the symbol for the common electrical devices and what the devices are used for.*

Listed below are a number of devices. For each one you have to match its correct circuit symbol with its correct function in a circuit.
An example has been done for you.

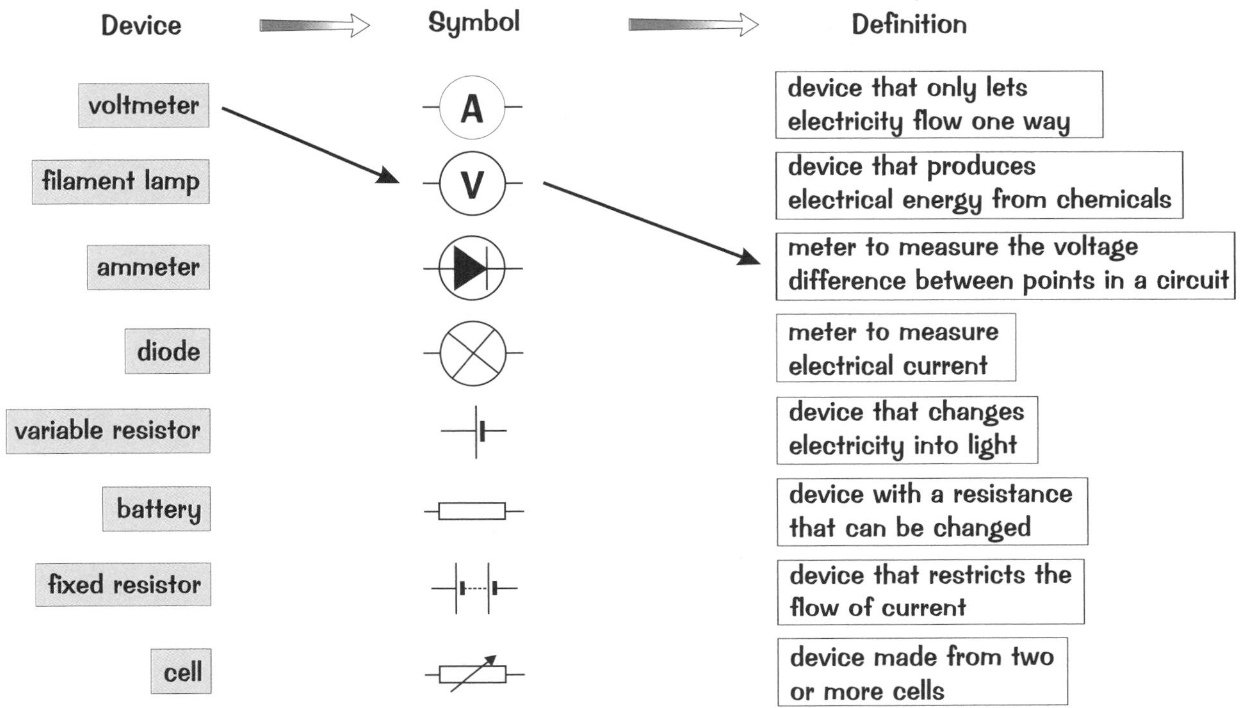

Q2 *This question is about a dimmer switch.*
Turning the knob clockwise (↻) makes the light brighter.
Turning the knob anticlockwise (↺) makes the light dimmer.

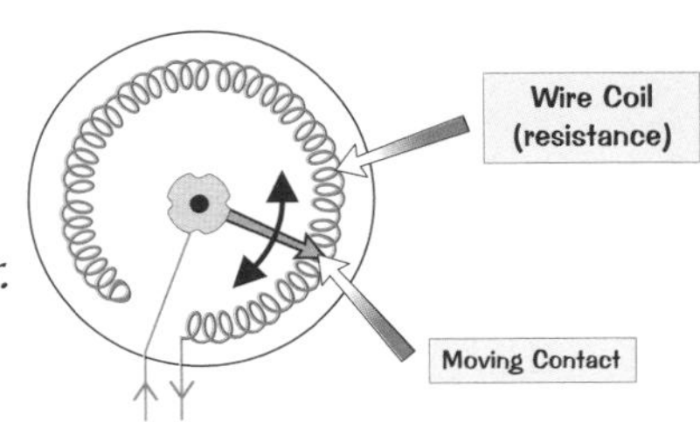

The 3 diagrams below show the dimmer switch at different settings. The arrows show the path that the electricity takes around the switches.

For each switch, write down how the light will appear.

Choose from:

DIM

MEDIUM BRIGHT

BRIGHT

a)

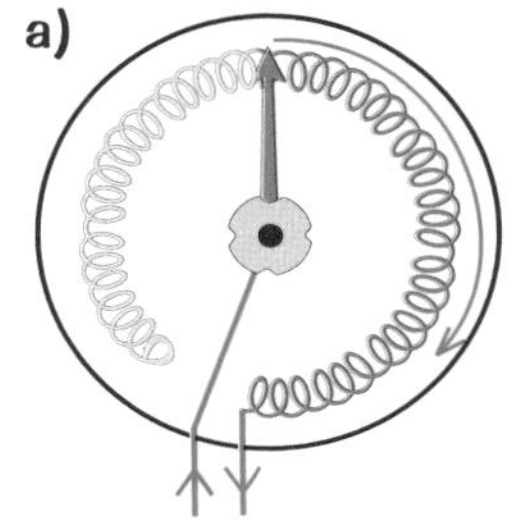

ANSWER: ________________

b)

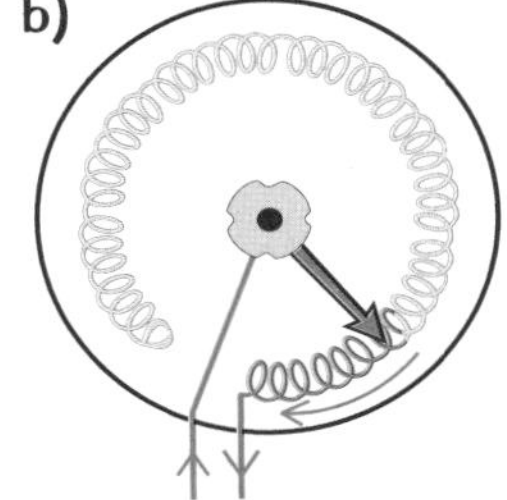

ANSWER: ________________

c)

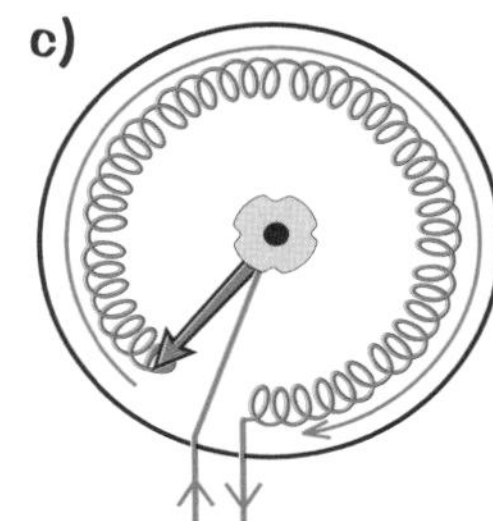

ANSWER: ________________

Questions on Series Circuits

Q1 Two circuits were connected up like in the pictures below. For each circuit, draw a circuit diagram in the spaces below, using the usual symbols for the components.

a)

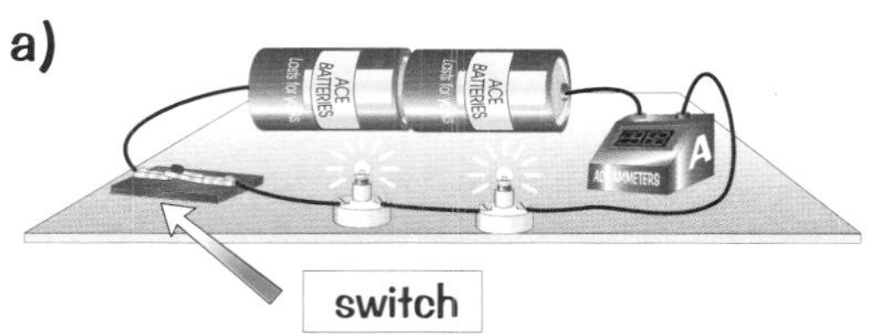

b)

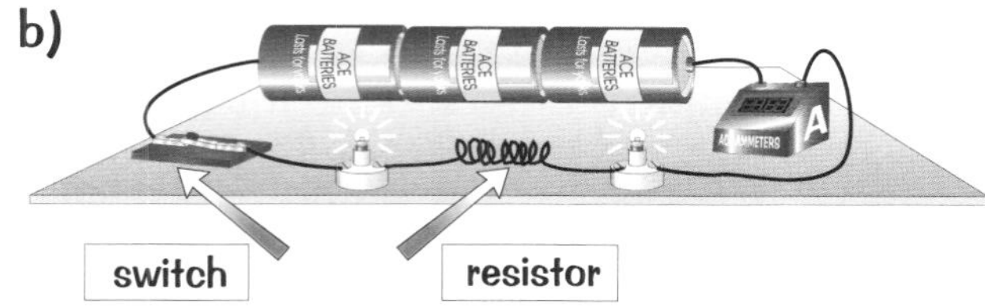

ANSWER

ANSWER

Q2 *Look at the circuit diagram opposite. It shows two cells with two lamps connected in series.*

With the circuit set up this way, the lamps are both at NORMAL *brightness.*

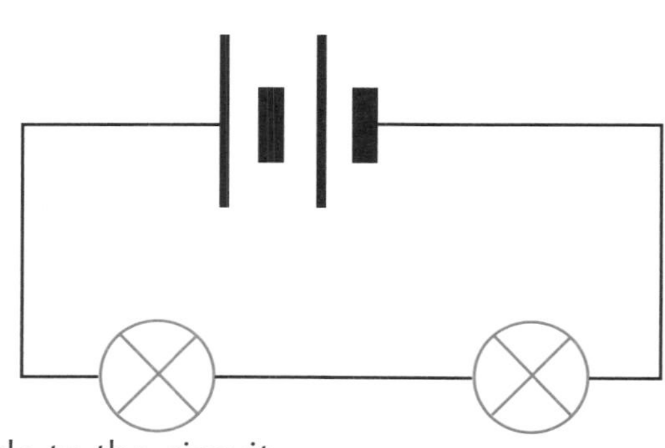

Listed in the table below are 6 changes that are made to the circuit.
For each change, work out what happens to the brightness of the lamps and just tick the correct column.

What is done to the circuit	Lamps are:			
	Off	Dim	Normal	Bright
a) one lamp is unscrewed				
b) one of the cells is turned round				
c) another cell is added, the same way round as the first two				
d) another cell is added, the opposite way round to the first two				
e) another bulb is added				
f) both of the cells are turned round				

Questions on Series Circuits

Q3 *Resistance in a circuit can be changed by combining resistors in series.*

In this question, you have to match up the combined resistors on the left with the single resistor that could replace them.

Just draw a line between the two that match.

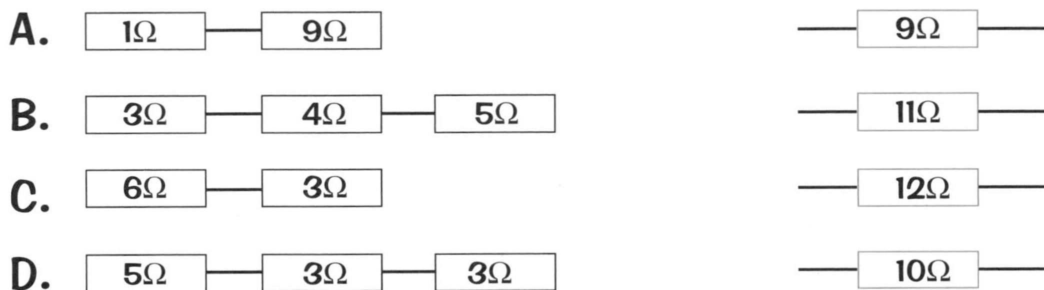

Q4 Fill in the gaps in the following paragraph. The words to use are in the grey box.

dimmer	each	smaller	higher

If lamps are connected in series, the current goes through _____________ lamp in turn. The more lamps you add, the _____________ they get. This is because the current has got _____________. Adding more lamps makes the total resistance _____________.

Q5 Study the circuit diagram on the right.

In each of the following questions some information is given.

Just circle the correct answer.

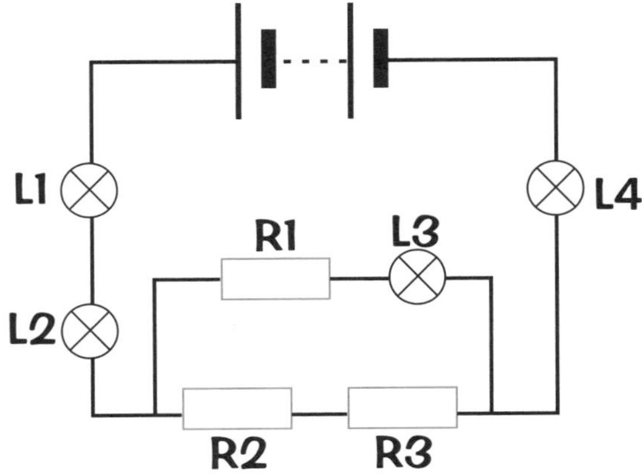

a) The current through lamp L1 is 2 amp. Is the current through lamp L2: 1 amp / 2 amps?

b) The current through lamp L1 is 2 amp. Is the current through lamp L4: 1 amp / 2 amps?

c) The current through lamp L3 is 1 amp. Is the current through resistor R1: 1 amp / 2 amps?

d) The current through resistor R2 is 1 amp. Is the current through resistor R3: 1 amp / 2 amps?

Questions on Parallel Circuits

Q1 *This question tests you on drawing parallel circuits.*
These pictures below show 2 parallel circuits.

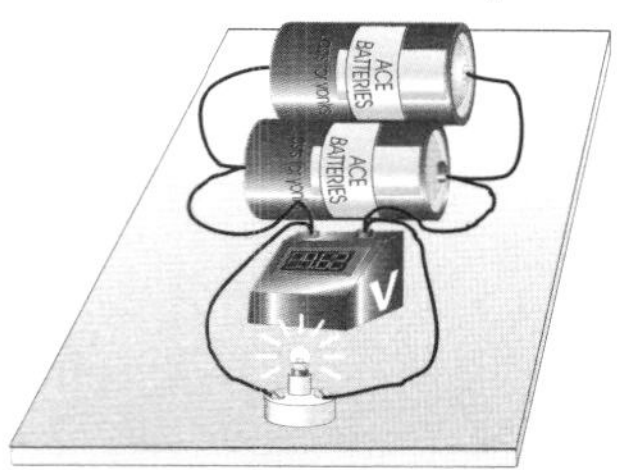

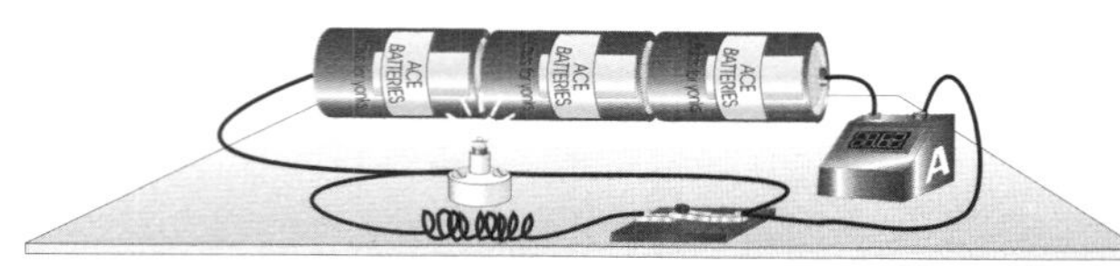

In the spaces below, draw the circuit diagram for each of the circuits.

ANSWER

ANSWER

Q2 *Look at the circuit diagram opposite. It shows two cells with two lamps connected in parallel.*

With the circuit set up this way, the lamps are both at <u>normal</u> *brightness.*

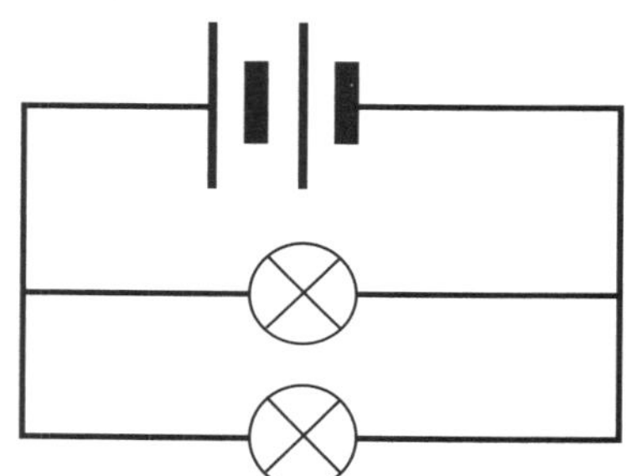

For each change to the circuit listed in the table below, work out what happens to the brightness of the lamps and tick the correct column.

What is done to the circuit	The lamps are:			
	Off	Dim	Normal	Bright
a) one lamp is unscrewed				
b) another cell is added in series				
c) another bulb is added in parallel to the first two				

Q3 *Look at the circuit diagram below.*

Decide what will happen to each of the three lamps when switches S1, S2 and S3 are altered.
– Just write in ON or OFF for each lamp.

	Switch			Lamp		
	S1	S2	S3	L1	L2	L3
a)	open	closed	closed			
b)	closed	closed	closed			
c)	closed	open	closed			

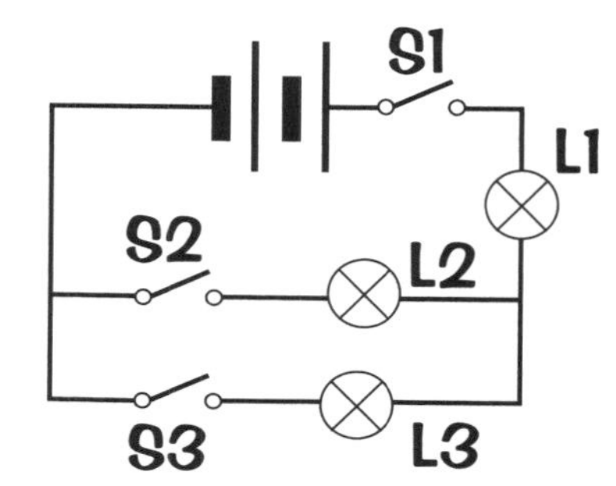

Questions on Parallel Circuits

Q4 Fill in the gaps in the following sentences. Use the words from the grey box.

splits	still work	does not change	branch	the same

When two lamps or resistors are connected in parallel, the potential difference across each one will be ____________________. The current ____________, so some goes to each ________________.

When more lamps are added in parallel, the brightness ____________________.

If one branch is incomplete, then the others __________________.

Q5 *These pictures show electric current coming to a split in a parallel circuit.*

a)

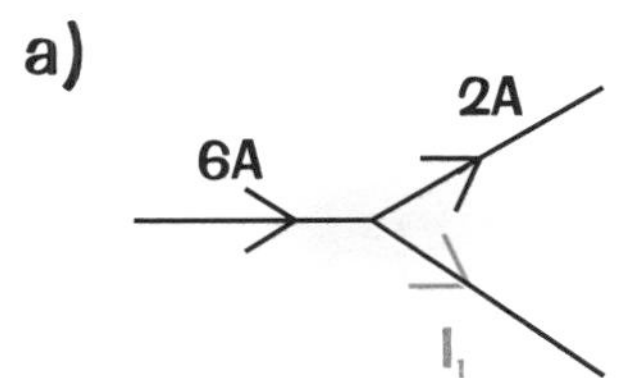

I_1 = ... amps

b)

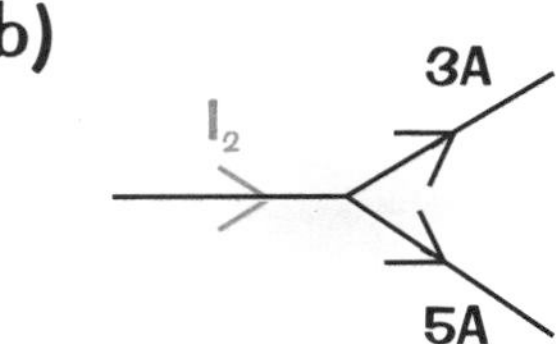

I_2 = ... amps

c)

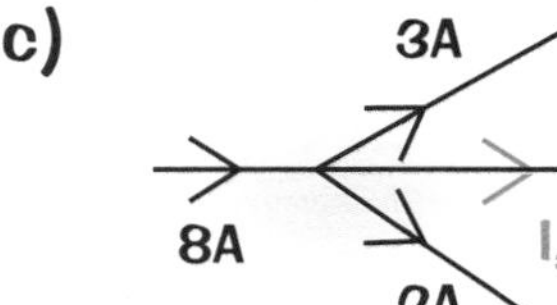

I_3 = ... amps

In each case, one of the current values is missing. Work out the missing values, I_1, I_2 and I_3 and write your answers in the boxes.

Q6 Look at this circuit diagram showing a parallel circuit.

Say whether each of the statements that follow are true (T) or false (F).

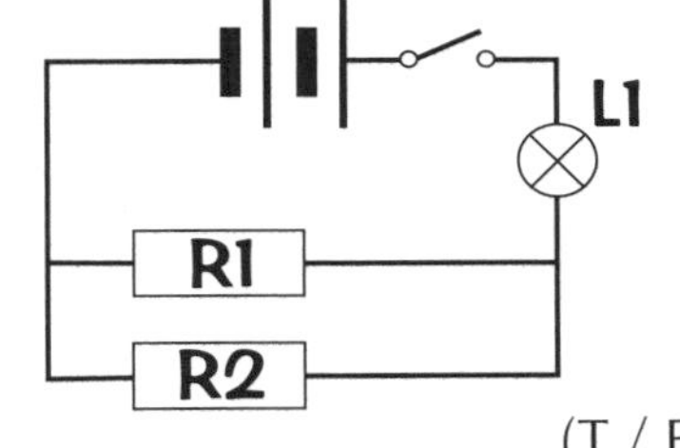

a) The two resistors R1 and R2 are connected in parallel. (T / F)

b) The lamp L1 and the switch are connected in parallel. (T / F)

c) The electric current is the same everywhere in the circuit. (T / F)

d) The potential difference across each resistor is the same. (T / F)

Q7 *This circuit diagram shows a number of lamps and ammeters. The readings on some of the ammeters are given.*
See if you can work out what the missing values are.

A1 = 5 amps: A2 = ... amps.

A3 = 2 amps: A4 = ... amps.

A5 = ... amps.

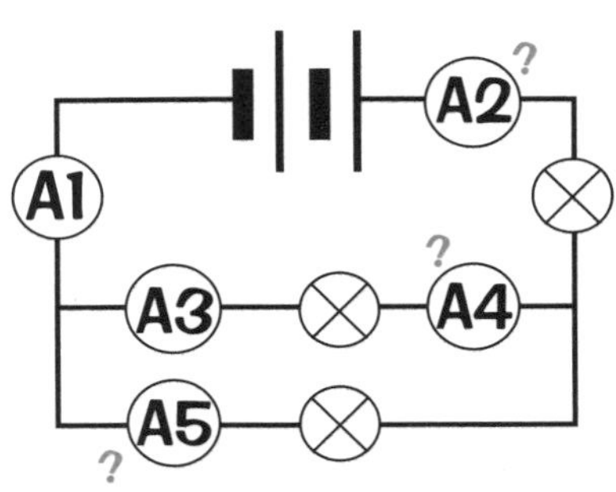

Questions on Static Electricity

Q1 Match up the statements below about static electricity. The first one is done for you.

a)	Static electricity is caused by	attract
b)	There are two types of charge called	the charges balance out
c)	In a normal, uncharged object	rubbing
d)	The only things that move when rubbing	repel
e)	Opposite charges will	are electrons
f)	Similar charges will	positive and negative

Q2 Below are two jumbled up sentences describing how a rod can be charged by rubbing it with a duster.

...the cloth to the rod.

...and the rod becomes

...positively charged.

...electrons are transferred from...

...negatively charged.

This means the cloth becomes...

If you rub an acetate rod with a cloth...

Write the sentences in the correct order. (Using scrap paper for rough working may help.)

....

....

....

Q3 Rubbing a polythene rod with a duster causes the rod to become negatively charged. The picture on the left shows the balanced charges on a rod and duster before rubbing.

Before rubbing → **After rubbing**

On the second picture, after rubbing, draw

a) where the charges have moved to.

b) the direction the electrons have moved.

Questions on Static Electricity

Q4 *Objects with unbalanced electric charges will either attract or repel.* Look at each of the pictures and say whether the rods will attract or repel.

A Attract or repel? ____________

B Attract or repel? ____________

C Attract or repel? ____________

D Attract or repel? ____________

Q5 Tim starts off with an uncharged polythene rod.

Fill in the gaps in the following sentences that he wrote about it.

positive	evenly	equal	no	negative	repel

This plastic rod carries ____________ overall charge. It carries ____________ numbers of ____________ charge and ____________ charge.

The similar charges don't clump together because they ____________ each other.

This means that the charges spread out ____________.

Q6 *A positively charged duster is held close to the rod.*
– Draw the new arrangement of the charges in the rod.

Q7 *Static electricity can be used to help spray paint a car door.*

Decide if the following statements are true (T) or false (F) and circle the correct answer.

a) The paint nozzle is connected to the positive terminal. (T / F)

b) This makes the paint drops have zero charge. (T / F)

c) The paint drops repel each other. (T / F)

d) The drops stick together. (T / F)

e) The car door has a negative charge. (T / F)

f) The paint drops are attracted to the car door. (T / F)

Questions on Energy in Circuits

Q1 Look at the circuit diagram on the right.

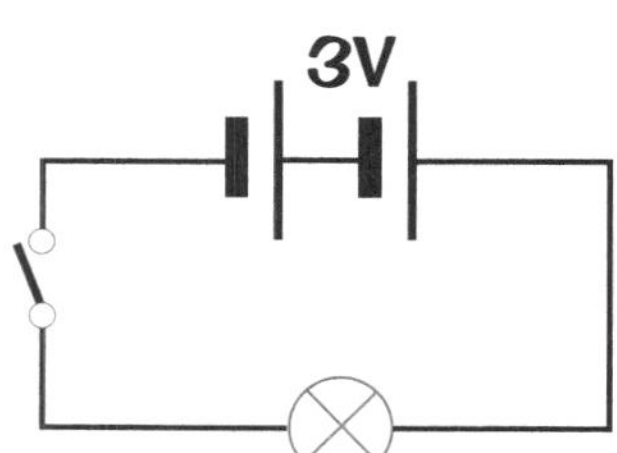

Now read the paragraph about this circuit and fill in the gaps using the words in the grey box.

brighter	incomplete	series	two	increased	current		
lamp	cells	heat	off	light	useful	electrical	wires

When the switch is closed, a __________ flows around the circuit and the __________ lights up. The 3V battery is made up of __________ 1.5V __________ connected in __________. The energy is transferred along __________ to the lamp. The lamp changes ____________ energy to __________ energy and _________ energy. The light energy is the __________ output.

If the switch is open, the circuit is __________, and the lamp is __________.

If the battery voltage is __________ to 6V, the lamp glows __________ and more energy is transferred than with the 3V battery.

Q2 *Electricity can easily be changed into other types of energy.*
Match up the device with the useful form of energy that it produces from electricity.

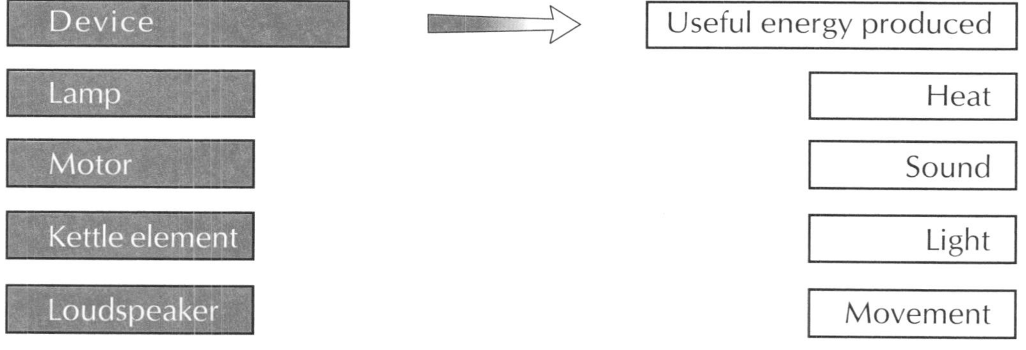

Q3 This question is a number of statements about electrical energy. All you have to do is to choose the right choice from the brackets and put a ring around it.

a) Electrical energy flows around a circuit as an electric (current / direction).

b) An electrical current is a flow of (atoms / charge).

c) When electric charge flows through a resistor, energy is transferred as (heat / sound).

d) We measure the amount of energy transferred in units called (amperes / joules).

e) The transfer of 1 joule of energy in a time of 1 second means the power is 1 (watt / volt).

Questions on Energy in Circuits

Q4 *Electrical power can be found in two different ways, depending on what information you are given. Written below are the two equations and formula triangles to work out electrical power.*

Power (W) = Potential Difference (V) x Current (A)   Power (W) = Energy (J) / Time (s)

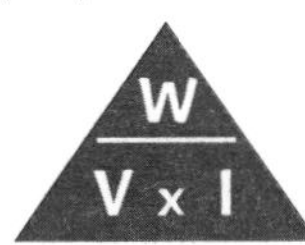

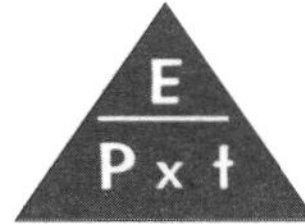

Now fill in the table below. You will need to use the first equation to complete the *Current* and *Power* columns, and the second equation for the *Energy* column.

Potential difference (V)	Current (A)	Power (W)	Time (s)	Energy (J)
3	0		6	
12		24	3	
12		48		96
240		2400	10	

Q5 This diagram shows a heating coil connected to a battery in a heating experiment. Readings are taken of the temperature every minute. The results are shown in the table below.

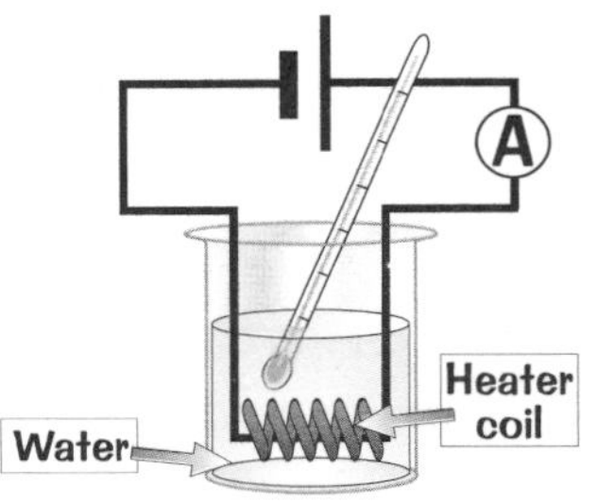

Time (minutes)	0	1	2	3	4	5	6	7	8
Temperature (°C)	20	40	58	71	82	89	95	100	100

a) Use the results from the table to draw a graph of temperature against time on the graph paper below.

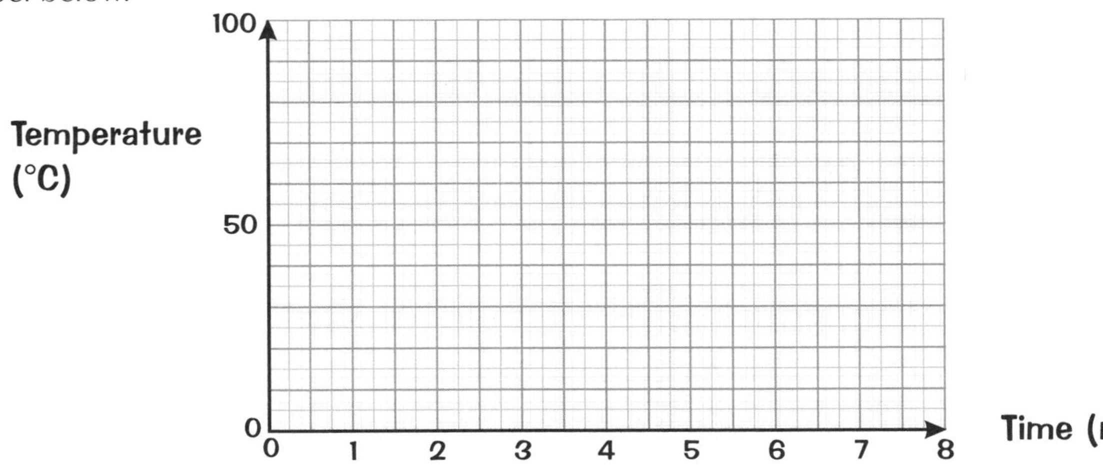

b) Estimate the temperature of the water after a time of 2.5 minutes. ....

c) What is the highest temperature that the experiment will get to? ....

Questions on the Cost of Domestic Electricity

Q1 Complete the following sentences about the cost of electricity.

joules	present	units	current	take	twice	energy

The cost of electricity depends on the number of ______________ that are used. To find the number, ______________ the previous meter reading from the ______________ meter reading. You pay for the ______________ that has been used, not the ______________ or the voltage. If the label on an appliance says "1kW", then it means it uses 1000 ______________ every second. A 2kW appliance will use energy ______________ as fast.

Q2 Look at the meter readings from these four houses.

Name:	Chrissie	Eleanor	David	Clive
Previous Reading	47041	26935	34628	51362
Present Reading	47525	27601	35109	57413
Units used:				

a) Use a calculator to work out the number of units of electricity each house has used. Write your answers in the boxes beneath the dials.

b) Who has used the most electricity? ....

Q3 *The true nature of a "unit" of electricity or the villain of your electricity bill unmasked!*

a) Circle the correct meaning of a unit of electricity in the list below.

Kilojoule	Watt-second	Kilowatt-hour	Kilojoule-hour

b) Listed below are 4 definitions of a unit of electricity. Tick the one correct definition.

It is when an energy of 1000 joules is used in 1 second. ☐

It is when a power of one watt is used for 1 second. ☐

It is when a power of 1000 W (1kW) is used for I hour. ☐

It is when an energy of 1 joule is used in 1 hour. ☐

Questions on the Cost of Domestic Electricity

Q4 *Changing between watts and kilowatts needs to be done sometimes.*

a) How many watts are there in 1 kilowatt? ....

b) How many kilowatts is 4000 watts? ....

c) How many watts is 3 kilowatts? ....

d) How many watts is 10 kilowatts? ....

Q5 Listed below are a number of different units.
Decide which are units of energy and which are units of power, then write them down in the correct column in the table below.

Megawatt	kW
J	Joules
watts	kiloJoules
W	kilowatt-hour
units	kWh
kilowatt	MW

Power	Energy

Q6 *This question is on working out the cost of using different appliances for different lengths of time.*
Complete the table below given that the cost of electricity is 10p per unit. Use the following equation —

Cost of Electricity = Units used × cost per unit

The first example is done for you.

Appliance	Power Rating (kW)	Time (h)	Units used	Cost of Electricity at 10p per unit
Storage Heaters	2	4	$2 \times 4 = 8$	$8 \times 10 = 80$p
Cooker	7	2		
1-bar Electric Fire	1	1.5		
Kettle	2	0.1		
Iron	1	1.2		
Refridgerator	0.12	24.0		
Lamp	0.06	6.0		
Radio Cassette	0.012	2.0		

Questions on Plugs and Fuses

Q1 *Plugs and fuses are used to protect people and electrical equipment from electrical faults and accidents.*

a) Three common electrical hazards are shown in the pictures below.

A) 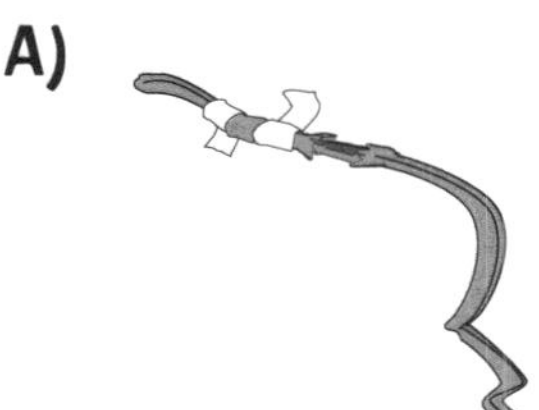

B) 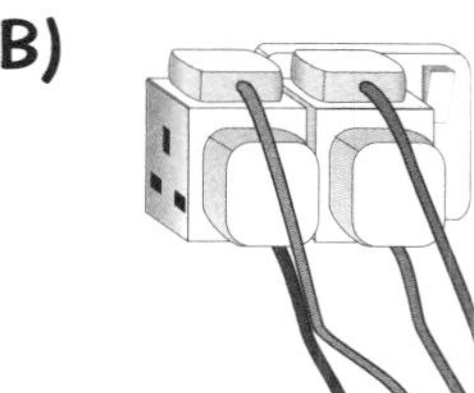

C) 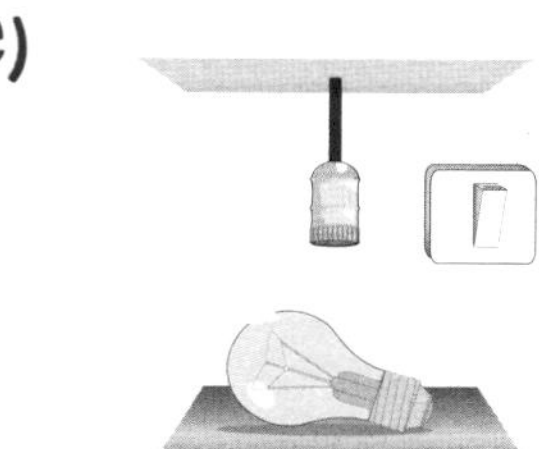

Read through the hazards below and write down the letter of the picture each one refers to.

i) Overloaded sockets are very dangerous. This is a fire risk. ....

ii) Leads should not be worn, frayed or cut. No bare wire should be exposed. ....

iii) Leaving bare connectors, or handling equipment still connected to a socket when the switch is on can be dangerous. ....

b) Read through the following actions that must be taken to remove the hazards in part **a)**. Then write down which of the pictures each one refers to.

i) Replace the worn leads, do not simply join the leads together. ....

ii) Replace sockets with double sockets, or use a multisocket block. ....

iii) Turn off the light and replace the bulb. ....

Q2 *The diagram below shows the inside of a domestic plug.*

Complete the labelling in the diagram.

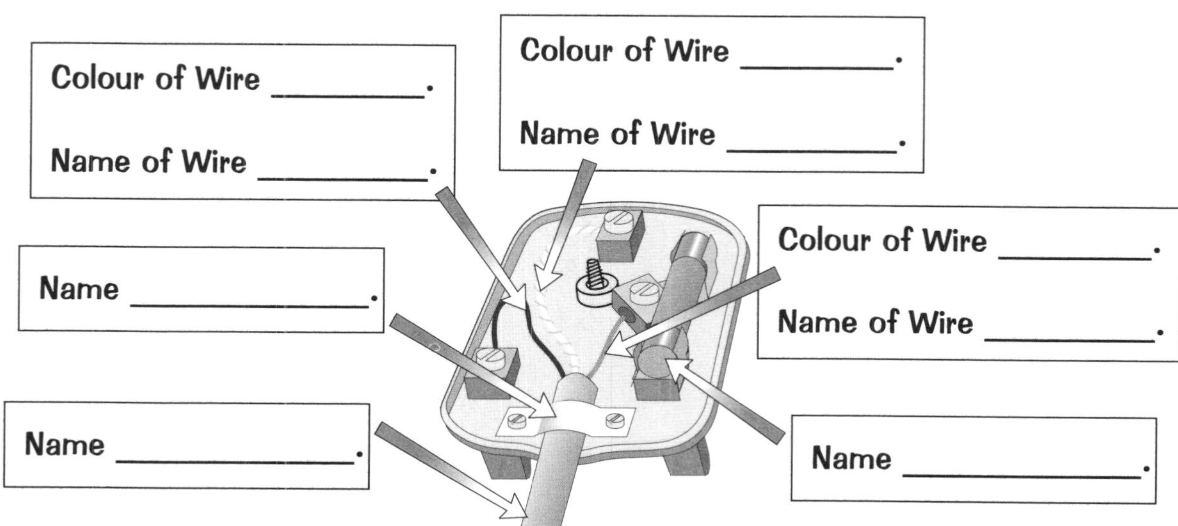

Questions on Plugs and Fuses

Q3 Use the words from the list of words in the grey box to complete the following sentences on wiring a plug.

fuse	conductor	three	plastic	grip	rubber	insulator	copper	brass

Electrical cable consists of two or ______________ inner cores of ______________. This is used because it is a good _____________. The outer layers are made from flexible ________________. This is used because it is a good ____________________.

The plug has a case made from plastic or ______________ because they are good insulators. The pins of the plug are made from _______________ which is a good conductor, and is quite hard.

A _______________ stops too much current flowing by blowing. A _________________ holds the wires in place in the plug so they can't be pulled out from the bottom.

Q4 *The table below shows 7 appliances and the current that passes through them.*

What you have to do is to choose whether a 3A, 5A or a 13A fuse needs to be fitted.

Write your answers in the table.

(the first one is done for you as an example)

Appliance	Current taken (A)	Fuse needed (A)
Food Mixer	2	3
Cassette Player	3	
Hairdryer	4	
Electric Heater	12	
Toaster	4	
Kettle	9	
Vacuum Cleaner	3.5	

Q5 *This diagram shows a kettle circuit that has been wired badly.*

Complete the sentences showing what's wrong with the circuit and the drawing.

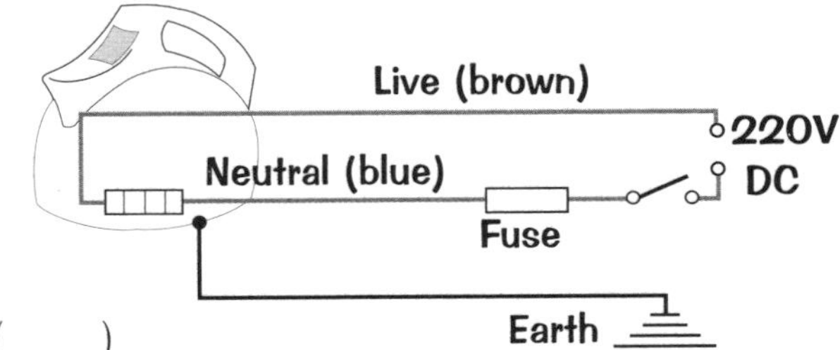

a) The voltage should be .... V. (.........)

b) The .... coloured wire should be connected to the fuse.

c) The switch should be on the .... wire.

d) The symbol for the earth should be ....

Questions on Mains Electricity

Q1 *The diagram below shows how electricity is made in power stations and sent to homes.*

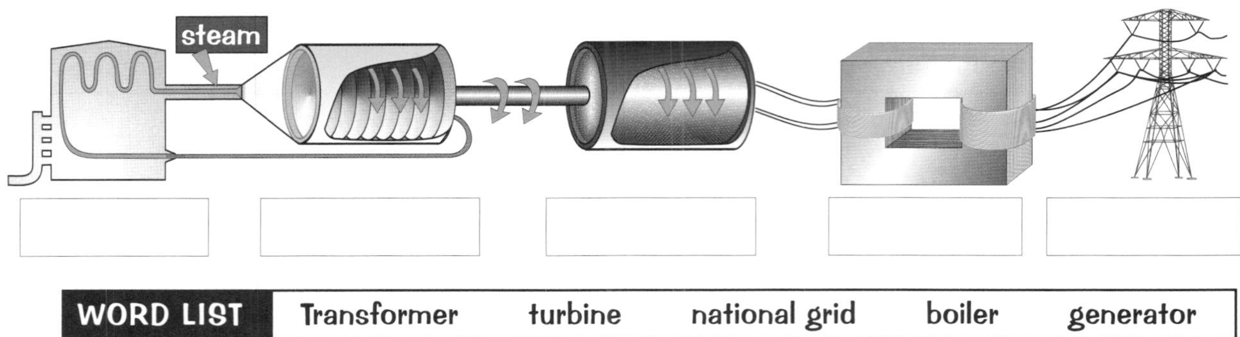

WORD LIST	Transformer	turbine	national grid	boiler	generator

Use the words from the WORD LIST to complete the *labels* on the diagram.

Q2 In the questions below, draw lines to pair up the Electrical Words with their Descriptions.

Electrical Word  Description

Electrical Word	Description
a) Transmit	rotary motor driven by steam
b) AC	place for generating and distributing electricity
c) DC	direct current
d) Turbine	send from place to place
e) Power station	changes the voltage of alternating current
f) Transformer	alternating current
g) Fuse	resettable device for cutting off electrical current
h) Circuit breaker	a thin wire that melts when the current is too high

Q3 *Complete the gaps* in the following paragraph about *electricity generation* using the words from the WORD LIST.

WORD LIST	steam electromagnet oil chemical natural gas generator coal nuclear turbine

Most traditional power stations change ______________ energy into electrical energy. The energy comes from the three main fossil fuels, ______________ , ______________ and ______________.

In a ______________ power station, energy comes from radioactive substances. In both kinds of station, the heat energy makes ______________ in the boiler. This drives a ______________ which makes a ______________ spin. This spins an ______________ in coils of wire. Electricity is made in these coils.

Questions on Mains Electricity

Q4 The power used (or "drawn") by a device can be worked out if you know the voltage across it and the current flowing through it.

a) Write down the formula for calculating power, P, given the voltage, V, and the current, I. Answer: ....

b) *Look at the circuit on the right which shows a resistor, R, connected to a 6V battery.* Find the *power* the resistor uses if the current is:

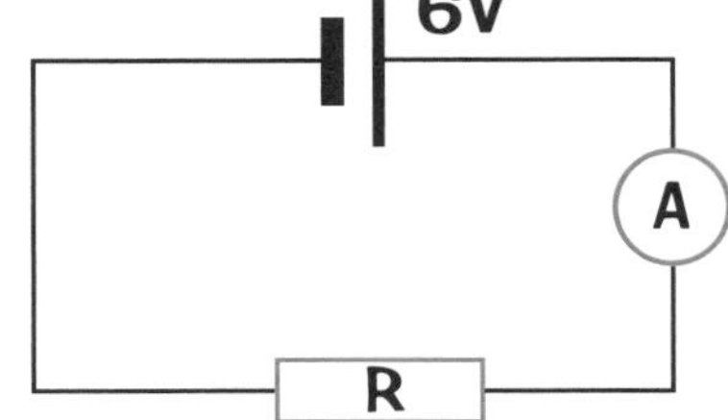

i) 3A ....

ii) 4.5A ....

Q5 Shown opposite is a circuit with a 12V battery and a 4Ω resistor.

a) Find the *current* supplied by the *battery* to the resistor.

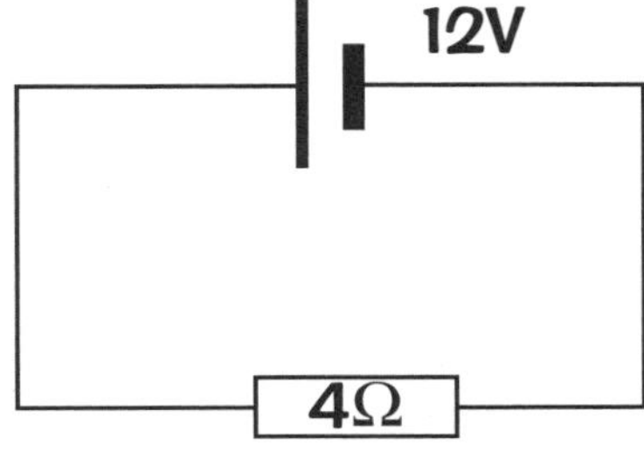

FORMULA NEEDED:

....

WORKING:

....

b) Find the power supplied to the circuit by the battery.

....

Q6 *The table below lists 3 electrical devices.*

Complete the *missing* information for the TV and the kettle. Take mains voltage as 230V. (The first one, for the *Iron*, has been done for you.)

Appliance	Power in kilowatts (kW)	Power in Watts (W)	Current in Amps (A)	Fuse: 3A or 13A?
Iron	0.920	920	3.8	13
TV	0.115		Formula needed ______ Working: Answer:	
Kettle	2.300		Formula needed ______ Working: Answer:	

Questions on Magnetic Fields

Q1 *The pictures below show 8 experiments with bar magnets and various materials*

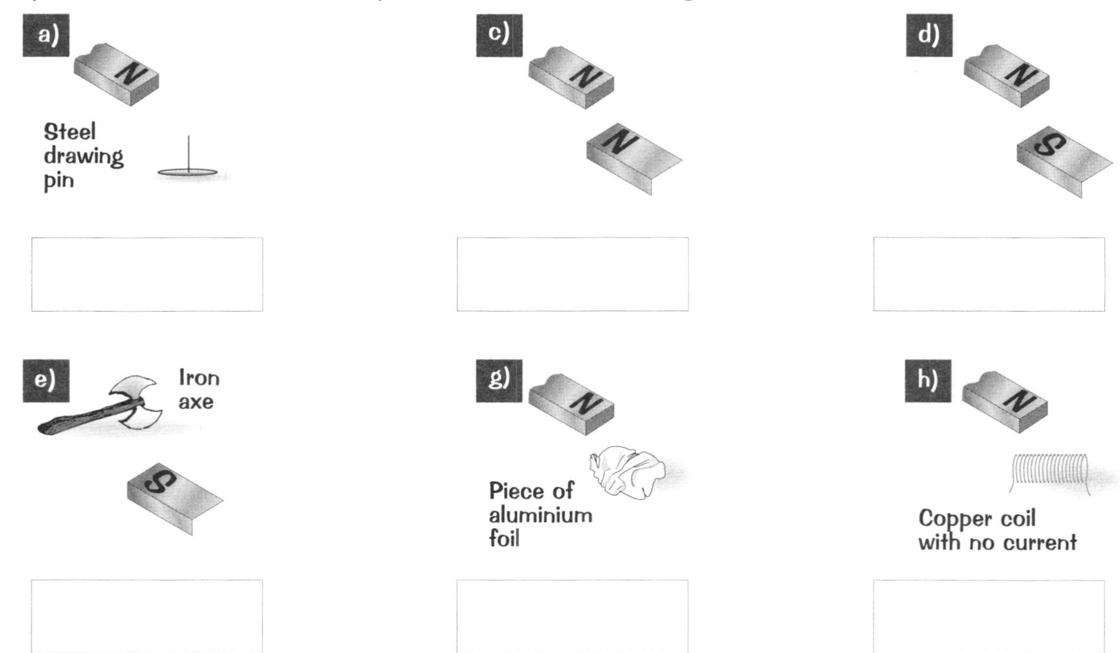

For each experiment, there is attraction, repulsion or no magnetic forces acting. Write down (in the boxes) your answer as _attract_, _repel_ or _none_.

Q2 Tick the materials below that are magnetic, and put a cross for the ones which are non-magnetic.

Iron	☐	Copper	☐	Aluminium	☐
Brass	☐	Leather	☐	Steel	☐
Silver	☐	Plastic	☐	Gold	☐
Nickel	☐	Wood	☐	Sulphur	☐

Q3 *Denise has a problem to solve. She has two magnets that do not have the poles marked on them; Magnet 1 and Magnet 2.*

Magnet 1 has a blue end and a red end.

Magnet 2 has a yellow end and a purple end.

Magnet 1

Magnet 2

She holds the ends of the magnets together to see if there is an attraction (A) or a repulsion (R).

She records her results in the table opposite.

Part of her results table is filled in. Complete the rest of it for her.

End of Magnet 1	End of Magnet 2	Force
Red	Purple	A
Red	Yellow	
Blue	Yellow	
Blue	Purple	

Questions on Magnetic Fields

Q4 Complete these sentences about magnets using the words in the grey box.

field	south	stronger	attract	two	seeking	poles	south	repel

Any magnet has ____________ oppositely behaving ends called ____________. If the magnet is left to spin freely, it will stop pointing in a north – ____________ direction. The end pointing north is called the north – ____________ pole. The other end is called the ____________ – seeking pole, or south pole for short.

Opposite poles ____________. Similar poles ____________.

The area around a magnet is known as the magnetic ____________. The stronger the magnet, the ______________ the field.

Q5 These pictures of magnetic experiments are not complete. You have to complete them.

a) This magnet has been left to spin. It has come to rest like this. Label the two ends of the magnet N and S according to the poles.

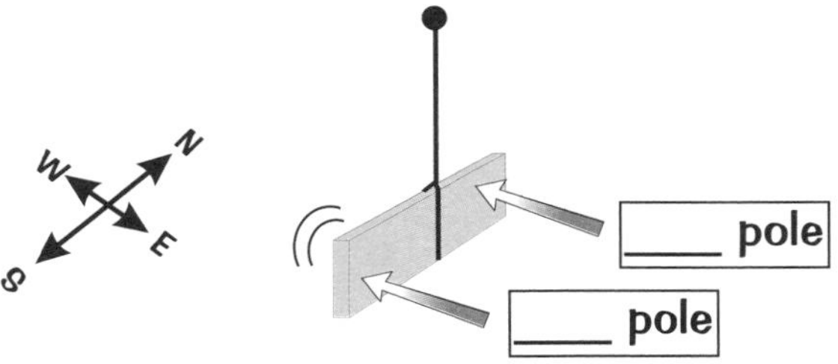

b) A bar magnet is chopped in half so that 2 new bar magnets are made. Label the poles on the new, smaller magnets.

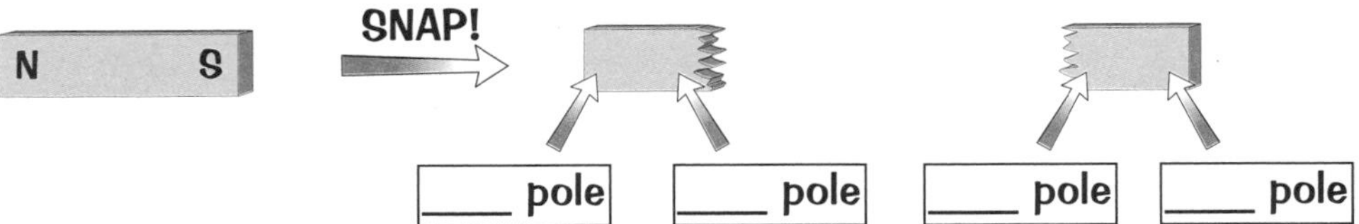

c) A strong bar magnet is brought close to an iron nail. The nail becomes a magnet. Label the poles on the nail magnet.

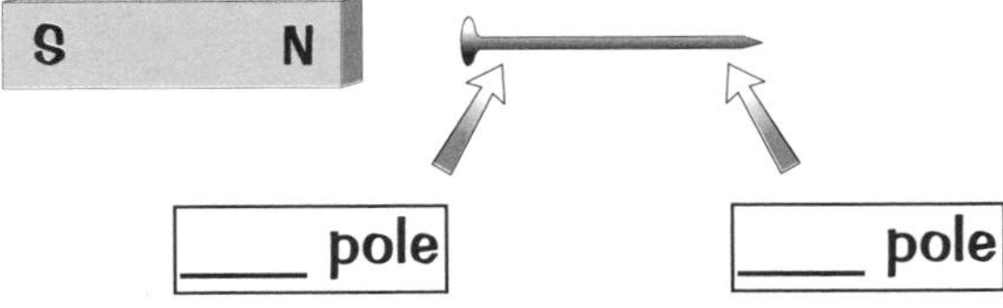

Questions on Electromagnetism

Q1 *Two pictures of a scrapyard electromagnet, a) and b), are shown on the right.*

Write down which of the circuits below, Circuit 1 or Circuit 2, is needed to operate the electromagnet in each case.

Circuit 1 **Circuit 2**

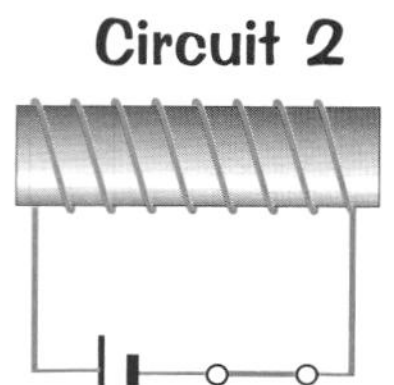

a)

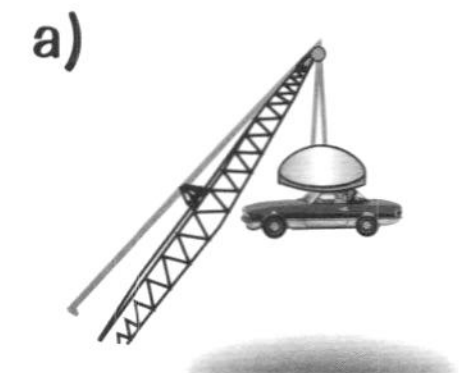

Circuit? __________

b)

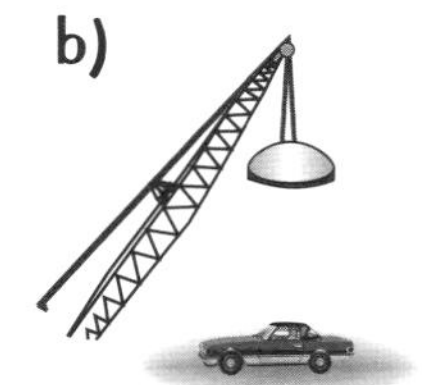

Circuit? __________

Q2 The diagram on the right shows a copper wire near the end of a bar magnet.

The wire is in the magnetic field produced by the magnet, and is carrying a current of 1A. There is a force on the wire because of the current and magnetic field.

David plans to make some changes to the experiment.

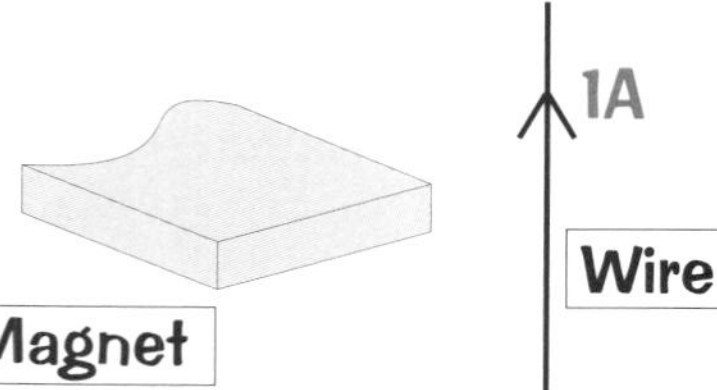

The table below lists 6 changes that David made.
For each change, show with a tick whether you think the force on the wire will increase, decrease or stay the same.

Change to experiment	The force increases	The force decreases	The force stays the same	The direction of the force changes
a) Change the current to 2A				
b) Use a stronger magnet				
c) Change the current to 0.5A				
d) Use an aluminium wire carrying 1A				
e) Reverse the current flow				

Q3 Look at this picture of an electric bell circuit.

Complete the description of what happens when someone presses the switch. Use the following words:

off	down	up	open	made
	closed	broken	open	

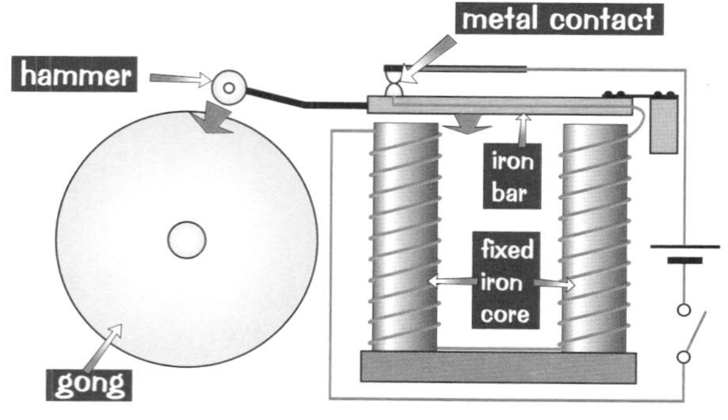

When the switch is __________ the electromagnets turn on. The iron bar is pulled __________. This clangs the gong. At the same time the contact is __________. The magnets go __________ and the arm springs back, ready to start again.

Questions on Electromagnetism

Q4 Circle the correct words in the brackets to complete these sentences about electromagnets.

a) An electromagnet will be stronger if the current through it is (higher / lower).

b) An electromagnet will be stronger if there are (fewer / more) turns on the coil.

c) An electromagnet will be stronger with a core made of (iron / wood / copper)

Q5 *When wire is wound into a long coil, we call it a SOLENOID.*
A group of 4 students have carried out an experiment to make solenoids — the details are below in the pictures.
All the coils are of the same size, and have the same current flowing through the wires.

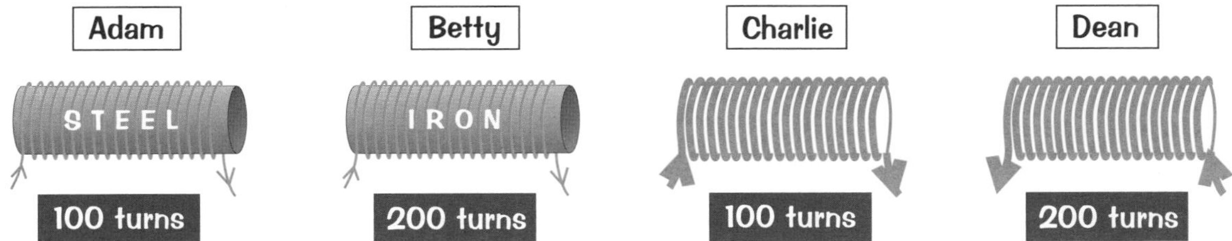

a) Which solenoid would give the strongest magnetic field? ....

b) Which solenoid would give the weakest magnetic field? ....

c) What sort of material would the wire be wrapped in? ....

d) Which solenoid would still be magnetic after the current was switched off? ....

Q6 The diagram below shows a circuit breaker.

a) Add these labels to the diagram.

pivot	brass contacts
spring	iron core
iron rocker	

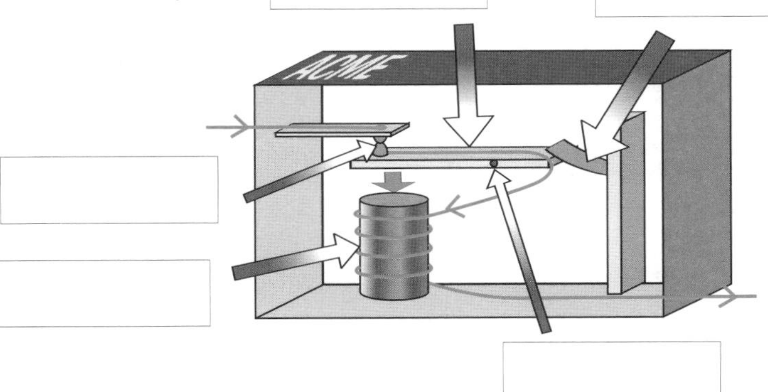

b) Rearrange the sentences to explain how the circuit breaker works.

1. they break the circuit if the current is too high.
2. Now it has to be reset manually.
3. As the iron rocker moves, the contacts separate, the switch is tripped, and the spring flips past the rockers so that the switch is held open.
4. Circuit breakers are fitted to the incoming live wire and
5. It does this because a large current allows the electromagnet to attract the iron rocker, despite the spring.

Correct order = ...

Questions on the Motor Effect

Q1 These are all things that work from electricity. Some of them have electric motors, some don't. Write (M) if they contain a motor and an (X) if they don't.

a) Vacuum cleaner ☐ **b)** Hair Dryer ☐

c) Digital watch ☐ **d)** Radio ☐

e) Electric Drill ☐ **f)** Video Recorder ☐

g) Kettle ☐ **h)** Loudspeaker ☐

i) Electric fan ☐ **j)** Electric blanket ☐

k) Fan oven ☐ **l)** Food mixer ☐

Q2 Look at this diagram of a simple electric motor that you may have made in the laboratory.

a) Choose the letters that correspond to the following parts.

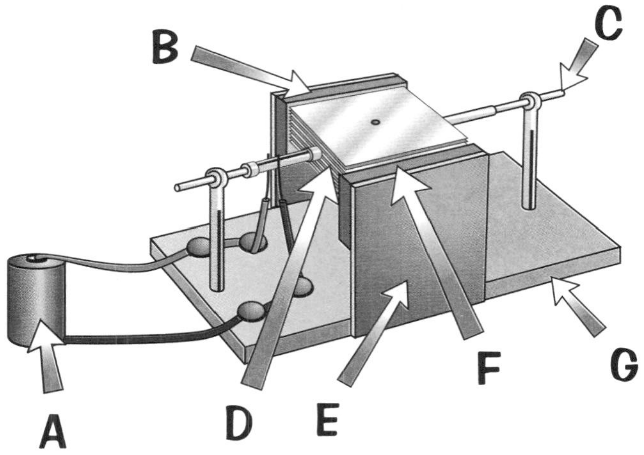

i) aluminium axle: ....

ii) base plate: ....

iii) power source: ....

iv) magnet holder: ....

v) turns of wire: ....

vi) 2 magnets: .... and ....

A B C D E F G

b) *The motor in part a) can be made to speed up or slow down.*

Read the following sentences and circle the correct answer.

i) Putting more turns of wire in the coils will make the motor turn faster / slower.

ii) Using weaker magnets will make the motor turn faster / slower.

iii) Increasing the current in the coils will make the motor turn faster / slower.

c) What device could you add to the apparatus above, to easily change the speed of the motor without altering the motor itself?

....

Questions on the Motor Effect

Q3 *The loudspeaker relies on electromagnetic forces as well.* Write down the order the following statements should go, to describe how a loudspeaker works.

a) This creates sound.

b) This makes the coil move backwards and forwards.

c) which is wound over the South pole of the magnet.

d) are fed into the speaker coil

e) the cardboard case vibrate.

f) These movements make

g) Signals from the amplifier

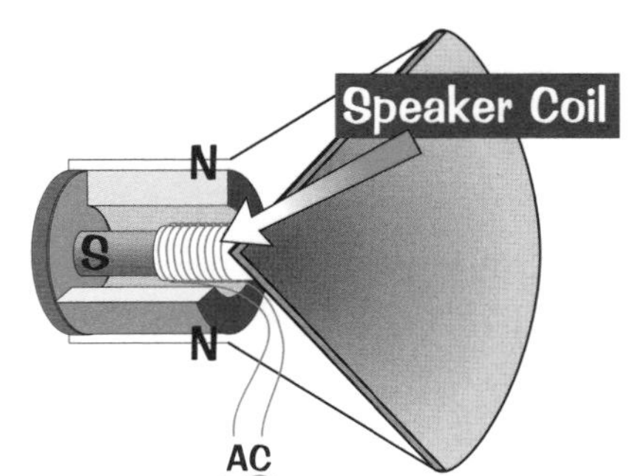

Correct order ....

....

Q4 *Study the diagram of an experiment opposite. A metal bar is resting on top of two metal wires, and the bar is free to move.*

When the current is switched on, the bar moves to the left.

Now read each of the changes made to the apparatus and indicate with a tick the direction the bar will move.

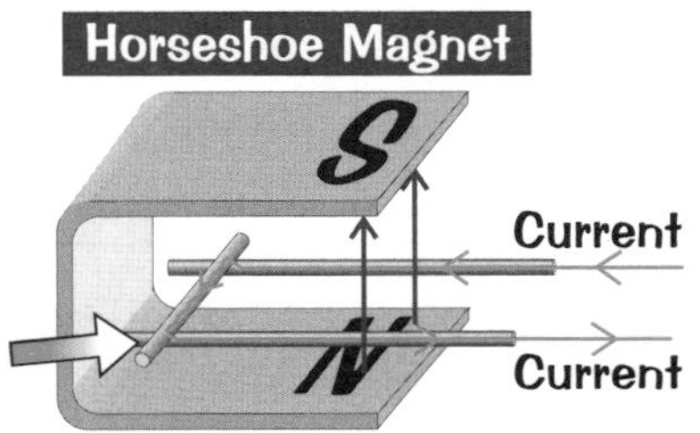

Change that is made	Left	Right	No movement
a) the current is increased			
b) the current is reversed			
c) the north and south poles are swapped			
d) a bar made of plastic is used instead			

Q5 Look at this picture of a bar magnet and a solenoid made of copper wire.

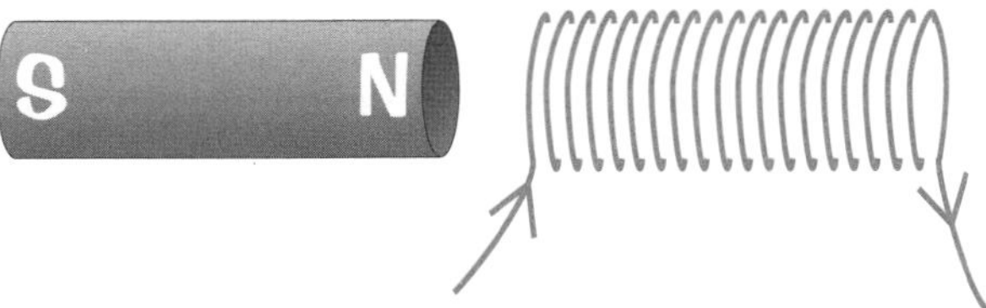

When the current is switched on and 1A flows through the coil, the coil is pulled towards the bar magnet.

Read each of the statements below and circle true (T) or false (F).

a) The end of the solenoid nearest the magnet must be a south pole. (T / F)

b) Increasing the current will make the force of attraction less. (T / F)

c) Changing the direction of the current will make the coil repel. (T / F)

Questions on Electromagnetic Induction

Q1 Angela is carrying out an experiment with a coil of wire, a bar magnet and a milliammeter *(see the diagram).*

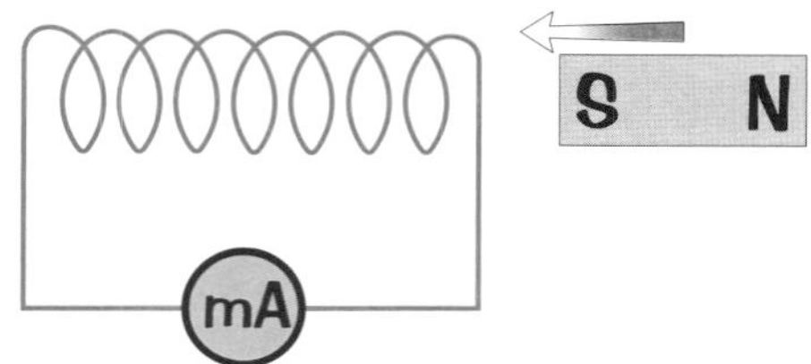

This is what the milliammeter reading looks like when the magnet is not moving.

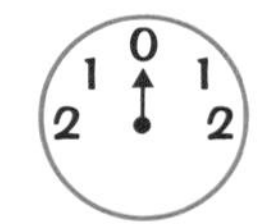

She moves the magnet into and out of the coil in different ways described in the table below, and writes down what happens to the needle on the milliammeter.

	Experiment	Needle goes
a)	North pole of magnet pushed in slowly from right	right, 1 division
b)	North pole of magnet pushed in quickly from right	right, 2 divisions
c)	South pole of magnet pushed in slowly from right	
d)	South pole of magnet pushed in quickly from right	
e)	North pole of magnet pulled out quickly to the right	

Complete the table by writing the direction the needle moves and the number of divisions it moves by.

Q2 *A model train set has a tunnel. A coil of insulated wire is wound around the tunnel and track as in the picture. A bar magnet is fixed to the top of the train, and the coil is connected to a buzzer.*

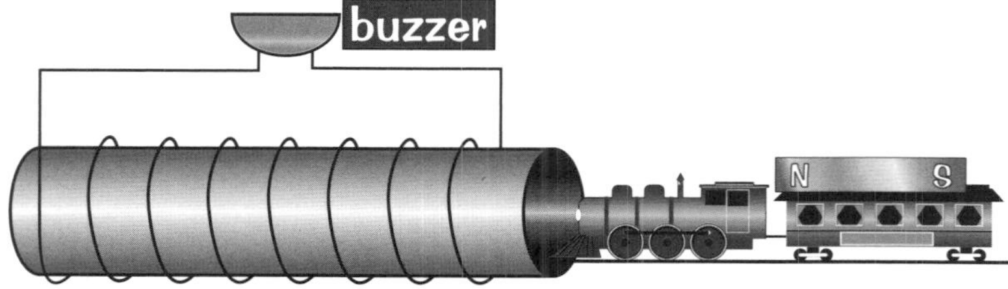

In each of the questions below, draw a circle around the correct answer from the brackets.

a) The buzzer sounds when the train goes through the tunnel because electricity is (absorbed / induced) in the coil.

b) If the train goes faster, there will be (more / less / the same) electricity produced, and the buzzer will sound (softer / the same / louder).

c) If the train stops in the tunnel, then the buzzer will be (louder / softer / silent).

d) Winding more coils on the tunnel will make the buzzer (louder / softer / the same).

e) Using a stronger magnet will make the buzzer (softer / louder / the same).

Questions on Electromagnetic Induction

Q3 Look at the picture opposite. A wire is moved upwards in a magnetic field as shown by the arrow — a current flows from X to Y.

a) If you use a stronger magnet, would the current be higher or lower? ....

b) If you move the wire more slowly, would the current be higher or lower? ....

Q4 *Electricity can be generated in coils of wire moving or spinning in a magnetic field. This is called electromagnetic induction — a voltage in the wire is induced.*

Fill in the gaps in the sentences below using the words from the grey box. They may be used more than once.

faster smaller greater

The induced voltage is affected by the magnets used. The stronger the magnet, the ___________ the induced voltage. If the coil only has a small area, then the induced voltage will be ___________. The ___________ the coil spins, the higher the induced voltage will be. Less voltage will be induced if the coil has a _________ number of turns.

Q5 Read the following descriptions, and decide whether they apply to simple generators, power station generators or dynamos. Just put a tick in the column.

	Description	Simple generators	Power station generators	Dynamos
a)	uses a spinning electromagnet			
b)	uses a rotating permament magnet			
c)	generates 25000 volts at 20000 amps			
d)	produces alternating current			
e)	produces direct current			
f)	spins 50 times a second			
g)	spins a magnet at different speeds			

Q6 Look at these oscilloscope traces. Match them to the descriptions below.

a) b) c) d)

A. Coil spinning slowly. ....

B. Coil spinning fast. ....

C. Coil resting. ....

D. Electricity from the battery. ....

Questions on Transformers

Q1 *A transformer is a device for changing the voltage of alternating current. The voltage entering can either be increased (stepped-up) or decreased (stepped down) — it depends on the numbers of coils wrapped around the two sides of the transformer.*

Look at these 4 transformers below.

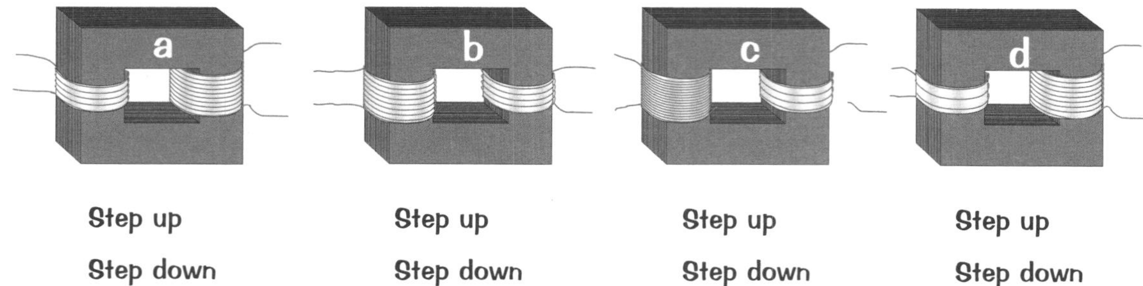

a	b	c	d
Step up	Step up	Step up	Step up
Step down	Step down	Step down	Step down

Which are step up, and which are step down? Just circle the correct answer. (The input is always on the left of the transformer).

Q2 *A model train set is connected to the mains supply via a transformer.*
A label on the transformer gives the following information.

Input:	230V	50Hz	12W
Output:	12V	1A	12W

Read the sentences below and circle the correct words in the brackets.

a) This transformer is a (step-up / step down).

b) The frequency of the mains supply is (50 / 1) times per second.

c) The power rating of the train set is (240 / 12) watts.

d) The current in the output circuit is (12 / 1) amps.

e) The current in the input circuit is (1 / 0.05) amps.

Q3 *Transformers are used to change the voltage of the electricity between leaving the power stations and entering factories and homes.*
— Power stations generate electricity at 25000 volts.

Write in the values of the voltage on the diagram below. Choose from:

230V	25000V	400000V	33000V

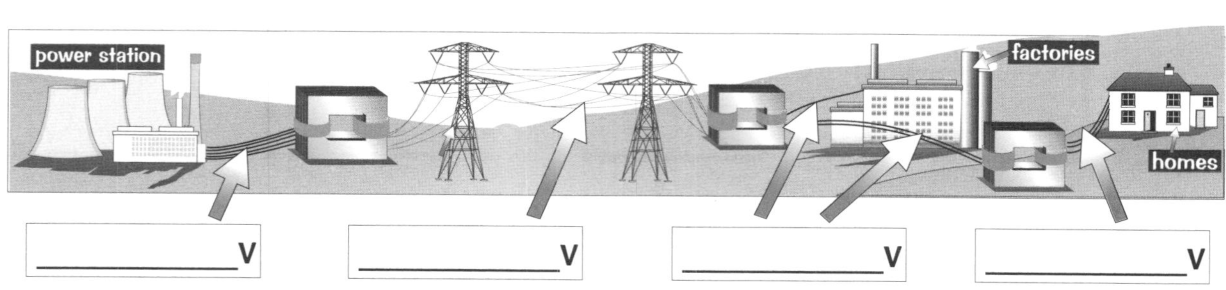

_____________V　_____________V　_____________V　_____________V

Electricity Revision A to Z

Well A-W actually. Find the following words, all to do with electricity. The first letter of each word begins with the question letter.

A) this is a meter for measuring electric current: ____________. (7 letters)

B) this is an energy source made from two or more cells: ____________. (7 letters)

C) a complete one of these is needed for electricity to flow: ____________. (7 letters)

D) this can make electricity by spinning a magnet in a coil: ____________. (6 letters)

E) this wire in a plug is coloured green and yellow: ____________. (5 letters)

F) a thin piece of wire that melts when the current is too high: ____________. (4 letters)

G) at the bottom of a plug, a cable ____________ holds the wires in place. (4 letters)

H) resistors produce this sort of energy when electricity flows through them: ____________ . (4 letters)

I) the sort of voltage produced in a wire moving near a magnet: ____________ (7 letters)

J) like all other types, electrical energy is measured in these: ____________. (6 letters)

K) this is known as a "unit" when you get an electricity bill:

____________ ____________. (8 letters and 4 letters)

L) this is the wire that is coloured *brown* in a plug: ____________. (4 letters)

M) compasses are made of small examples of these: ____________ . (7 letters)

N) this is the wire that is coloured *blue* in a plug: ____________. (7 letters)

O) if there is no circuit, then all components will be ____________. (3 letters)

P) in this arrangement of bulbs, they can be turned off one by one:

____________. (8 letters)

Q) if a device has a high power, it uses energy ____________. (7 letters)

R) this electrical device slows down electricity, and makes heat: ____________. (8 letters)

S) this is another possible arrangement of bulbs, one after another: ____________. (6 letters)

T) in a plug, the earth wire connects to this terminal: ____________. (3 letters)

U) when something is charged, the positives and negatives are

____________. (6 letters)

V) this meter is used to measure the potential difference in a circuit: ____________. (9 letters)

W) this is the basic unit of electrical power: ____________. (4 letters)

Question on Mass, Weight and Gravity

Q1 Fill in the *gaps* in the following passage using the **WORD LIST** below:

WORD LIST **ALL masses, mass, larger, attraction, weak, stronger, field, centre, newtons, weight, small, attracted**

Gravity is the force of ________________ between ______ ___________. For example, you have gravitational attraction to the person sitting next to you, and them to you. However, it is very _________ because the _________ of a person is relatively small. The mass of a planet is much larger and so its gravitational force is much ______________. The region in which the Earth's gravity can be felt is called the Earth's gravitational ___________. Any object in this region is ________________ to the Earth, which is what gives the object a ___________ – measured in ____________ and always acts towards the centre of the Earth.

Q2 *Complete* the table for mass and weight, by putting the sentences below in the *correct column*.

- amount of matter
- measured in newtons
- measured by a balance
- not a force
- measured by a spring balance
- is a force
- caused by the pull of gravity
- same anywhere in the universe
- measured in kilograms
- is lower on the moon than on Earth

Mass	Weight

Q3 a) Write down the formula relating *mass*, *weight* and *acceleration due to gravity*.

.... = ... × ....

Use this formula to solve the following questions and remember that the strength of gravity on EARTH is 10 N/kg.

b) Work out the WEIGHTS of the rocks with these masses in the spaces provided.

i) 5kg : .... Weight = ...

ii) 2.5kg : .... Weight = ...

iii) 120kg : .... Weight = ...

Questions on Mass, Weight and Gravity

Q4 Calculate the *masses* of rocks with the following weights.

i) 450N : .... Mass = ...

ii) 5N : .... Mass = ...

iii) 120N : .... Mass = ...

Q5 *"A bag of flour weighs one kilogram."*
This sentence is *wrong scientifically* speaking. Write a *correct version* of this sentence in the space provided. ....

Q6 a) *The strength of gravity on the moon is 1.6N/kg, not 10N/kg as on Earth.*
Write the *weights* these rocks would have if they were on the *Moon*.

i) 5kg : .... Weight = ...

ii) 2.5 kg : .... Weight = ...

iii) 120kg : .... Weight = ...

Compare these values with those you calculated in Q3(b). What do you notice?

....

b) Write the *masses* these rocks must have if their weights are measured on the *Moon*.

i) 16N : .... Mass = ...

ii) 960N : .... Mass = ...

iii) 124N : .... Mass = ...

Q7 The mass and weight of a spaceman, a space module and a rock are measured on Earth, before all three leave for the Moon. When they get to the Moon, the weight of each is again measured. *Fill in* the gaps in the following sentences by choosing the correct *masses* and *weights* of all three from the list below.

10,000kg 1kg 50kg 500N 16,000N 10N 100,000N 80N 1.6N

SPACEMAN : mass ______, weight on Earth ______, weight on Moon _______.

MODULE : mass _________, weight on Earth _________, weight on Moon _________.

ROCK : mass ______, weight on Earth ______, weight on Moon _______.

Questions on Force Diagrams

Q1 Draw in lines to connect the *forces* with their relevant *definitions* and *examples*.

TENSION	Acts straight down — eg on a person on Earth.
GRAVITY or WEIGHT	Slows things down — eg a car moving through air.
LIFT	In a rope or cable — eg a car towing another car.
THRUST (or PUSH or PULL)	eg the vertical force in an aeroplane wing.
REACTION FORCE	Speeds things up — eg from a rocket engine.
DRAG (or AIR RESISTANCE or FRICTION)	Acts upwards from a horizontal surface

Q2 *Michael's Dad's car will not start and he is trying to push it into the garage.*

a) The car is *not moving* — what then is true about the *forces* on it *overall?*

....

b) What two *vertical forces* act on it?

....

c) In which *direction* does each one act?

....

d) *Michael's dad is certainly putting a horizontal force on the car.* What *force* is balancing this to stop it moving.

....

Q3 *A car is moving in a straight line with a steady speed.*

a) Draw the two *vertical forces* on the diagram and label them.

b) Draw the two *horizontal forces* on the diagram and label them.

c) What is true about the two *vertical* forces?

....

d) What is true about the two *horizontal* forces?

....

Q4

After jumping out of an aeroplane, a sky diver accelerates until they reach a steady vertical velocity, called TERMINAL VELOCITY.

Draw in the two *vertical forces* when the diver is at TERMINAL VELOCITY and *label* them.

Questions on Force Diagrams

Q5 *The diagrams below show a submarine in the sea. The arrows on the sub represent forces — the longer the arrow, the bigger the force.* If the sub starts with a certain forward velocity, which way will it accelerate when it's acted on by the different forces in (a) – (f)?

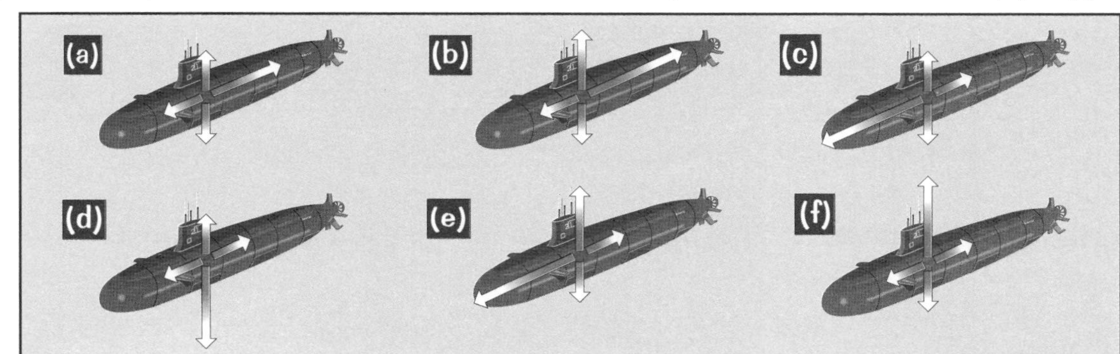

Example

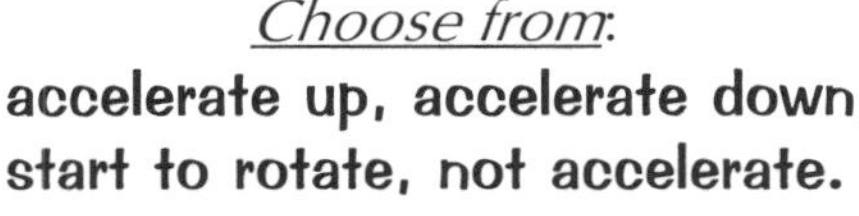

down only

a) ....

b) ....

c) ....

d) ....

e) ....

f) ....

Q6 *The planks a) to d) have forces pushing on them.*
Decide how *each plank* will accelerate and write your answer in the space provided.

> *Choose from:*
> **accelerate up, accelerate down, start to rotate, not accelerate.**

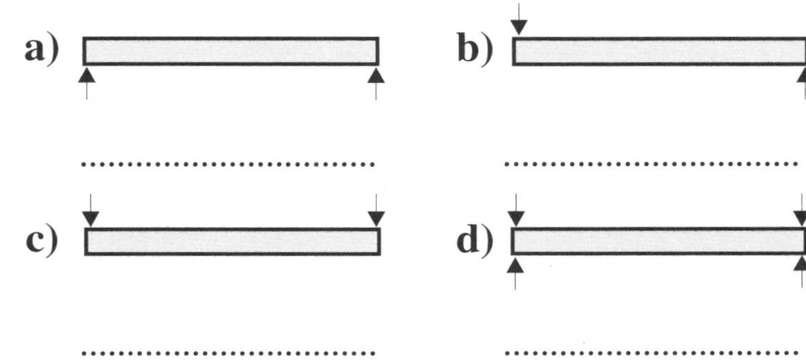

a) ....

b) ....

c) ....

d) ....

Q7 Use the words from the list of words in the box, *fill in* the gaps below. You can use each word ONCE, MORE THAN ONCE or NOT AT ALL.

> **equal motion balanced unbalanced opposite stationary speed overall straight slow fast change velocity same accelerate constant**

If the forces on an object are ______________, it will remain ______________ or move with a ___________ speed in a ______________ line (that is it will have ____________ velocity). Two forces are ______________ if they are __________ in size and in ______________ directions. An _____________ force is called a resultant force. If the forces are ______________, the _____________ of the object will change: it will ______________ up (______________), __________ down or ______________ direction. Also, the bigger the resultant force the more rapid the change in ____________.

Questions on Friction

Q1 *Damon is driving his new remote controlled car around a track on a patch of tarmac. When Damon's car goes round a corner, the grip between the tarmac and the tyres stop it sliding off the track.*

a) What is this *type* of friction called?

....

Unknown to Damon there is a patch of oil further up the track, and when his car "hits" it, it begins to skid across the tarmac.

b) What has the oil done to the *amount* of frictional force available from the tarmac?

....

c) Name the type of friction *now* occurring between the car tyres and the tarmac.

....

Damon's friend, Michael, has the same sort of remote controlled car, except with a much smoother, streamlined body.
His car goes quite a bit faster — what must this different body have *reduced?*

....

d) Give *two more* examples of where *reducing* this type of friction is useful.

....

Q2 *Complete* these sentences using the WORD LIST below,

against reduces increases balances accelerating kinetic heat wear lubrication

Friction is a force which acts ______________ the direction of movement. It always ______________ speed. Air resistance of an accelerating object ______________ until it ______________ the driving force and the object stops ______________.
Friction converts ______________ energy to ______________ energy. It also causes ______________ of the surfaces which are in contact. Friction between surfaces, especially those in machinery, can be reduced by ______________.

Q3 Complete the table below with the words **low** or **high** to show what the *ideal amount* of friction in the following cases should be.

Example of Friction	Friction should be...
A car tyre in contact with a road surface	
A skater moving over the ice	
Brake blocks pressing against a wheel rim	
Rock climbing boots in contact with the rock	

Questions on Friction

Q4 *Eddie starts off on his bike. Pedalling as hard as he can he reaches 20m/s, but does not get any faster than that.* Complete these sentences using the words below to describe what's happening in terms of *forces:*

friction	balanced	forward	faster	slow down
increase	equal	accelerate	increases	constant

a) As he is starting off, his pushing force is much greater than ______________.

b) This causes him to ______________.

c) As his speed increases total____________ also increases.

d) It will eventually become ____________ to the pushing force.

e) When this happens the horizontal forces are _____________.

f) This means that he will travel at a ____________ speed.

g) If he applies his brakes this _____________ the force of ___________ and he will

_________ _________.

h) If he starts going down a hill this will ____________ the ____________ force and he will

go ___________.

Q5 For each of these activities, say whether it will *increase* or *decrease* friction, and give *one* reason why it is done.

Activity	Increase or decrease friction	Reason
Skiers wax their skis		
Machines have to be lubricated with oil		
Climbers wear rubber-soled shoes		
Ballroom dancers wear leather-soled shoes and dance on a polished floor		
Footballers have studs on their boots		

Questions on The Three Laws of Motion

Q1 *Newton's First Law of motion is about the idea that balanced forces mean no change in velocity.* For each of these sentences write TRUE or FALSE in the space provided.

a) "balanced forces" means all the forces on an object are in the same direction. ☐

b) constant speed is the same as constant velocity . ☐

c) any object moving at a constant velocity has balanced forces on it. ☐

d) any change in direction is a change in velocity. ☐

e) an object moving in a curve must have a resultant (unbalanced) force on it. ☐

f) if forces are balanced they all act in the same direction. ☐

g) a resultant force is one which is not cancelled by another force. ☐

Q2 Draw a *circle* around the trucks below, where the forces acting are *balanced*.

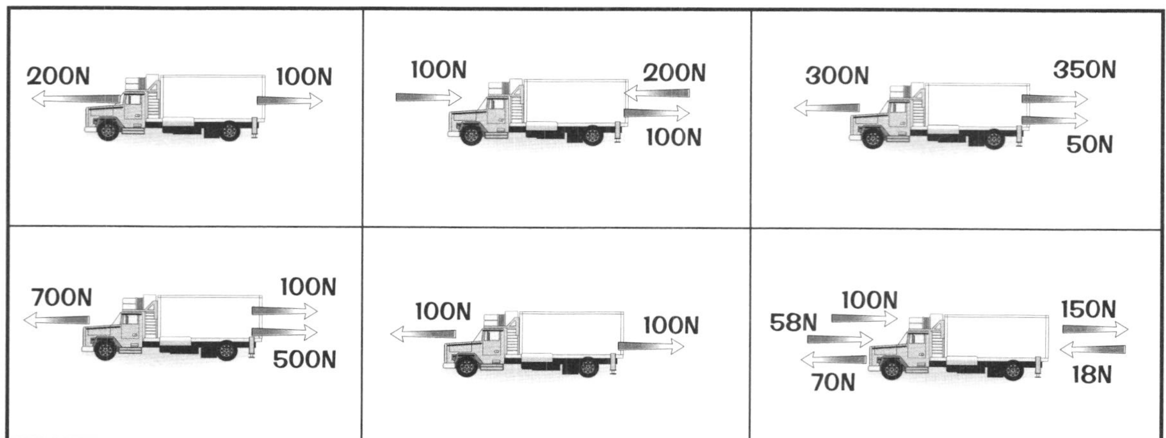

Q3 *Newton's Second Law of Motion is all about resultant (unbalanced) forces and acceleration*
Complete the following sentences about this law using the list of words in the box below.
You may use each word ONCE, MORE THAN ONCE or NOT AT ALL.

smaller	unbalanced	m	less	F	acceleration	same	different
accelerate	mass	more	bigger	resultant	a	acceleration	

An ______________ force (called a ______________ force) ALWAYS causes an object to ______________. The ______________ happens in the ____________ direction as the resultant force, and it's size depends on the size of the force and the ____________ of the object. The formula which describes this relationship is:

____ = _____ / _____

This means that if a force acts on small object, the ________________ is __________ than it would be for the same force acting on a large object would. Also, this means that if the mass stays the same, then a bigger force produces a ______________ acceleration.

Questions on The Three Laws of Motion

Q4 *Circle* which of these are forms of *acceleration*. (There are 5 in total.)

starting moving at constant speed changing direction
slowing down speeding up being still stopping finishing

Q5 *The triangle for working out this sort of thing is shown in the diagram.*

F / m x a

Complete these sentences:

a) F stands for ____________. **b)** a stands for ________________.

c) m stands for ___________. **d)** increasing F ______________ a.

e) increasing m ________________a.

Q6 Use the formula triangle in Q5 above to *complete* this table.

Force (N)	Mass (kg)	Acceleration (m/s^2)
	10	5
20		0.5
15	3	

Q7 *The pictures A to D show four galloping horses. The horizontal forces are shown.*

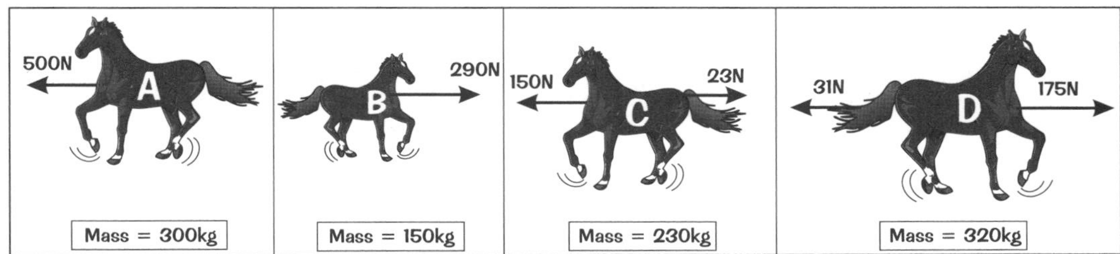

a) Work out the *resultant force* acting on:

Horse A .... Horse B ....

Horse C .... Horse D ....

b) Work out the *acceleration* of:

Horse A .... Horse B ....

Horse C .... Horse D ....

Q8 *Newton's Third Law of motion states that if object A exerts a force on object B, then object B exerts an equal and opposite force on object A.*

The hand in the diagram opposite is pulling a car on a rope. Draw and label an arrow on the diagram to show the force exerted *by the rope* on the hand.

Questions on Speed and Velocity

Q1 *Below are three formula triangles for speed, distance and time.*

A s / d × t

B t / d × s

C d / s × t

a) Which one is the correct version? ....

b) Use the correct triangle to write *versions* of this equation for:

SPEED	=	______	/	TIME
DISTANCE	=	______	__	______
TIME	=	______	__	______

So we can work out any of these three quantities, given the other two —

Q2 What is the *speed* for:

a) A racing car zooming a distance of 240m in a time of 3s?

FORMULA SPEED = ... / ....

WORKING ....

ANSWER Speed = ... m/s (Units)

b) A tortoise with a twisted ankle, shuffling 10m in 100s?

FORMULA SPEED = ... / ....

WORKING ....

ANSWER Speed = ... ______ (Units)

c) Are we working out *average speed* or *actual speed?*

....

Q3 Bernie the greyhound is running race which is 450m long. If he runs at 14m/s, *how long* will it take him to complete the race?

FORMULA TIME = ... / ....

WORKING ....

ANSWER Time = ... ______ (Units)

Questions on Speed and Velocity

Q4 *How far* would a racing car get travelling at 60m/s for 30s?

FORMULA DISTANCE = ... × ....

WORKING ....

ANSWER Distance = ... [ ] (Units)

Q5 *Miguel goes on a cycle ride. For 2.5 hours he travels at an average speed of 14km/h.* Work out *how far* he travels in kilometres (not metres as usual).

FORMULA DISTANCE = ... × ....

WORKING ....

ANSWER Distance = ... [ ] (Units)

Q6 *Complete* the following sentences:

"Speed is how ____________ you are going with no regard to ________________.

Velocity however must also have the _______________ specified."

Q7

a) Which of these have the same *speed?* ....

b) Which of these have the same *velocity?* ....

Q8 Draw two cars in the boxes below, and draw arrows to show their *velocities*.

One car is travelling at 30m/s EAST. The other is travelling at 30m/s NORTH.

N ↑

N ↑

Questions on Acceleration

Q1 *Complete* this passage about acceleration using the **WORD LIST**:

WORD LIST	metres negative m/s^2 velocity squared losing deceleration gaining speed time m/s second

If an object is accelerating its ________________ is changing. Usually "acceleration" means that an object is ____________ ________________. An object slowing down has a ________________ acceleration or _______________. Acceleration is worked out from the formula:

Change In ____________ / ____________Taken For Change

Its units are _________ per ____________ ____________ or in symbols _________.

Q2 Complete these sentences by *circling* the correct answer in the brackets:

If a motorbike has a steady **[acceleration / speed]** of $3m/s^2$ then every **[second / minute]** its **[speed / distance]** increases by **[3m/s / 3km/s]**. If it was decelerating, then its **[speed / distance]** would be **[increasing / decreasing]**.

Q3

Time (s)	0	1	2	3	4	5
Speed of X (m/s)	2.0	4.0	6.0		10.0	
Speed of Y (m/s)	17.5	15.0	12.5		7.5	

a) *Complete* this table for objects X and Y that accelerate and decelerate steadily.

b) What is the *acceleration* of X?

FORMULA ACCELERATION = ... / ....

WORKING ....

ANSWER Acceleration = ... ☐ (Units)

c) What is the *deceleration* of Y?

FORMULA DECELERATION = ... / ....

WORKING ....

ANSWER Deceleration = ... ☐ (Units)

Questions on Acceleration

Q4 What is the *acceleration* of Ben the cat pouncing from 0m/s to 5m/s in 4s?

FORMULA ACCELERATION = ... / ....

WORKING ....

ANSWER Acceleration = ... ☐ (Units)

Q5 *Complete* this sentence:

The change in speed of an accelerating object can be worked out from:

CHANGE IN SPEED = ________________ X ________________

Q6 A car has a *steady acceleration* of 2m/s^2. If it starts from rest, what is its *velocity* after 10s?

FORMULA CHANGE IN SPEED = ... X ....

WORKING ....

ANSWER Change in speed = ... ☐ (Units)

Q7 Put a *tick* by the correct formula for working out the *time taken* for a change in speed.

TIME = ACCELERATION / CHANGE IN SPEED ☐
TIME = ACCELERATION x CHANGE IN SPEED ☐
TIME = CHANGE IN SPEED / ACCELERATION ☐

Q8 *How long* does a motor bike take to stop if it is travelling at a speed of 16m/s and has a *steady deceleration* of 2m/s^2?

FORMULA TIME = ... / ....

WORKING ....

ANSWER Time = ... ☐ (Units)

Questions on Distance/Time Graphs

Q1 *This question is about a distance/time graph describing the motion of a car.*

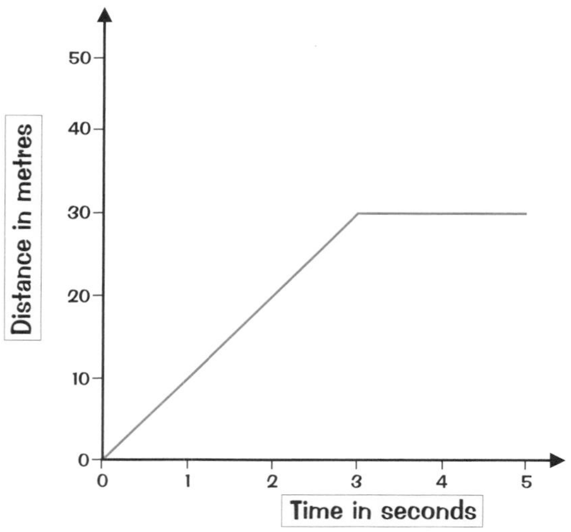

a) *How far* does the car move in the first *three seconds?* ....

b) What is the *speed* of the car during the first three seconds?

....

....

c) What is the car doing between 3 secs and 5 secs?

....

d) On the graph *draw a line* showing the motion of the car in the first three seconds if it was travelling at *half* the speed.

Q2 *The graph opposite shows the journey of Miguel the cyclist..*

a) *How far* does Miguel travel during the first 20 seconds of his journey?

....

b) What is his *speed* during this time?

....

....

c) *Describe* Miguel's journey between 20 and 40 seconds. (Is he going faster or slower than before? Has he stopped?)

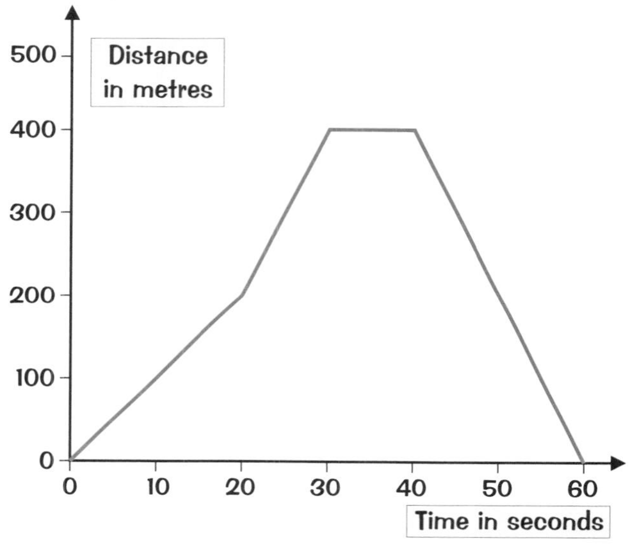

....

....

d) What is happening between 40 and 60 seconds?

....

e) What is the *total distance* travelled by Miguel over the whole 60 seconds?

....

f) How can you tell just by looking at the graph where his speed was *greatest?*

....

Questions on Velocity/Time Graphs

Q3 *The graph opposite is a velocity/time graph of an object.*

a) For each section *write down* the motion of the object.
Choose from:

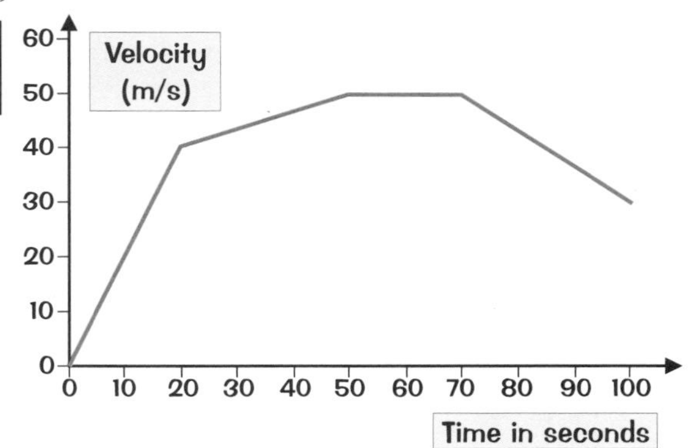

0 - 20s shows ....

20 - 50s shows ....

50 - 70s shows ....

70 - 100s shows ....

b) What is its *change of speed* between 20 and 50s? ....

c) Using your answer to part (b) work out its *acceleration* between 20 and 50 seconds.

....

d) If the object has mass 1000kg, what *force* would be needed to produce the acceleration in part (c)? (Hint : $F = m \times a$) ....

Q4

Velocity (m/s)	0	4	8	12	16	20	24	24	24	12	0
Time (s)	0	2	4	6	8	10	12	14	16	18	20

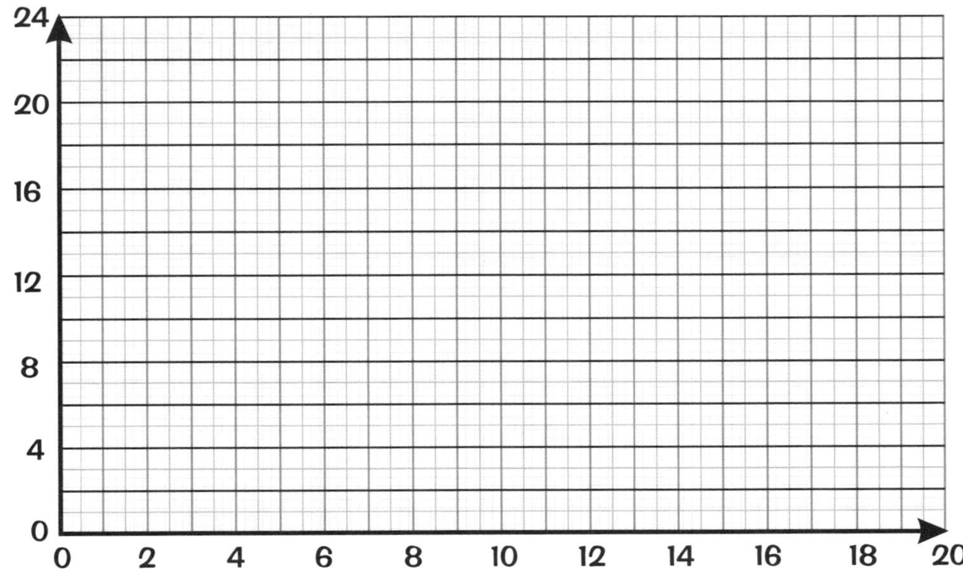

a) *Draw* the velocity/time graph using these measurements taken during a car journey. Make sure you *label* the axes correctly (with units too).

b) *Describe* the motion of the car by *writing on the graph* next to the lines you have drawn. Use words like steady acceleration, constant speed, etc.

c) By looking at ONLY THE GRAPH (no calculations) write down between what times *deceleration* is greatest. ....

Questions on Resultant Force and Terminal Velocity

Q1 *Complete the following sentences* using these words:

adding subtracting resultant forces direction overall motion same accelerate decelerate steady

In most real situations, there are at least two ____________ acting on an object in any one ______________. The ____________ effect of these forces will decide the ____________ of the object — whether it will ____________, ______________ or stay at a ______________ velocity. The overall effect is found by ____________ or ____________ the forces which point along the _____________ direction. The overall force you get is a ____________ force.

Q2 *A car has an engine which will produce a driving force of 4,500N.*

a) If its mass is 1500kg, what will its *acceleration* be? (Hint : Remember F = m × a so a = F/m)

....

b) As the car *increases* speed then this is no longer the case. What *increases* as the car goes faster?

....

c) At 70mph the *resistive force* acting on the car is 4450N. What is the size of the *resultant force* at this speed?

....

d) Use your answer to part (c) to work out what the car's *acceleration* will be at 70mph.

....

....

e) Complete this sentence, by *circling* the correct word in the brackets, to say what will happen as the car continues to accelerate:

"At 70 mph the acceleration of the car is very [***large / small***], but it is still gaining [***speed / mass***]. As speed continues to increase, [***resistance / acceleration***] will also increase.

Eventually the [***resistance / speed***] force will be [***equal to / much bigger than***] the driving force and there will be no [***resultant / gravity***] force. This means that the forces on the car are [***balanced / unbalanced***] and the car will move with a [***steady / changing***] speed."

Questions on Resultant Force and Terminal Velocity

Q3 *Opposite is a diagram of a parachutist.*

a) Add arrows to show the *two vertical forces* and *label* them.

b) The graph below is a velocity-time graph for the parachutist from the moment he leaves the plane until he arrives on the ground.

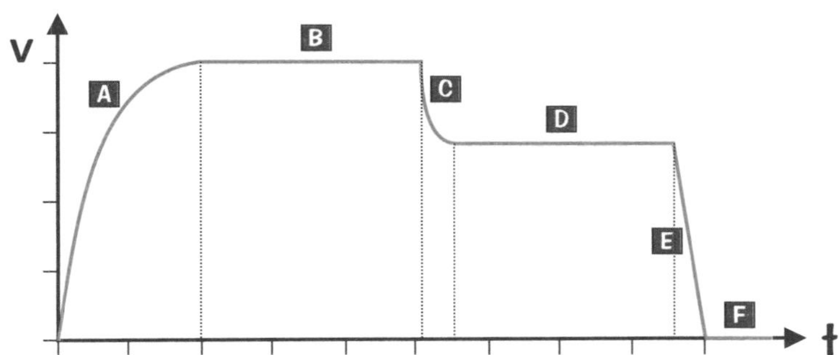

For each area of the graph write *what type* of motion is shown. Choose from the phrases in the box below:

constant speed constant acceleration constant deceleration changing acceleration changing deceleration stationary

Area A shows ....

Area B shows ....

Area C shows ....

Area D shows ....

Area E shows ....

Area F shows ....

Q4 For each of the statements (a) — (e), put a **T** in the box if they are **true**, an **F** if they are **false**.

a) A feather and hammer would land at different times if dropped from the same height on the moon ☐

b) Acceleration equals force times mass ☐

c) The size of the drag force depends on shape and area of the object ☐

d) Drag and weight are equal for an object falling at its terminal velocity ☐

e) Terminal velocity of a sky diver is the same whether his parachute is open or not ☐

f) As speed increases, drag force also increases ☐

g) When a car starts moving from rest, its resistive force is at a maximum ☐

h) The bigger the resultant force, the bigger the acceleration (when mass is the same) ☐

Questions on Stopping Distances

Q1 *Complete* the passage below using the words in the box below. You can use any word ONCE, MORE THAN ONCE or NOT AT ALL.

brake	braking	stop	constant	increases	maintains	decelerating	stopping	thinking

"The total distance a car takes to stop is called the ____________ distance. This is made up of two parts: the ____________ distance and the ____________ distance. The ____________ distance is the time before the driver actually starts to ____________. During this time the car ____________ its speed. The ____________ distance is the distance travelled from when the brakes are first applied, to when the car comes to a ________. The car will be ________________ as it travels this distance."

Q2 Give *three* examples of things (about the driver or the car) which would *increase* THINKING distance.

i) ....

ii) ....

iii) ....

Q3 Give *three* examples of things which would *increase* BRAKING distance.

i) ....

ii) ....

iii) ....

Q4 Which of these will take a *longer* distance to stop? Write the *number* of your answer in the space provided and choose whether *thinking distance*, *braking distance* or *both* are affected by this difference (write **T** for thinking distance, **B** for braking distance). The first one is done for you.

1	2	Which takes longer?	What is affected?
My car travelling at 50mph	My car travelling at 70mph	2	T and B
My car when I am ill	My car when I am well		
A car with four people and luggage in it	The same car with only a driver		
A car driving on a dry day	The same car on a wet day		
A car with new tyres	The same car with worn tyres		
A car with worn brake discs	The same car with new brake discs		

Questions on Stopping Distances

Q5 *The diagram below shows the stopping distances for cars at various speeds*

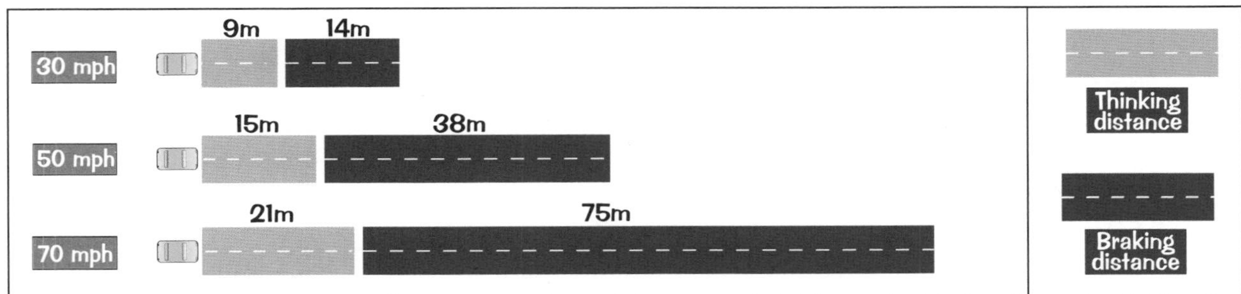

Using the diagram, *fill in* the Distance column of the table below. The first one has been done for you.

Speed of car	Type of Distance	Distance (m)
70 mph	total	96
30 mph	braking	
50 mph	thinking	
30 mph	total	
30 mph	thinking	
70 mph	thinking	
50 mph	braking	
70 mph	braking	
50 mph	total	

Q6 *This table shows stopping distances for speeds in m/s rather than mph.*

Speed m/s	Speed mph	Thinking distance (m)	Braking distance (m)	Stopping distance (m)
15	34	9	19	
20	45	12	30	
25	56	15	48	
30	67	18	70	

a) *Fill in* the Stopping Distance column in the table above.

b) On the axes opposite, *draw and label* the graphs for *"Thinking Distance"*, *"Braking Distance"* and *"Stopping Distance"*.

c) Does your graph suggest that Stopping Distance depends more upon *Thinking Distance* or *Braking Distance*?

....

....

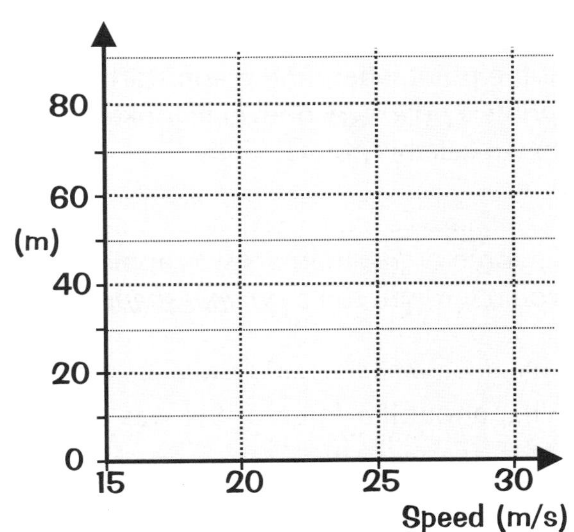

Questions on Hooke's Law

Q1 Use these words to *complete the following paragraph*. You may use each word ONCE, MORE THAN ONCE or NOT AT ALL.

length	force	mass	extension	increase	decrease	original	loaded

"Hooke's law states that extension is proportional to load. That means, if you pull something with a steadily increasing ____________ then the _____________ will _____________ steadily too. The important thing in a Hooke's Law experiment is to measure ____________ not total _____________. Extension is the length _____________ minus the ______________ length with no ___________ applied."

Q2 *Opposite are some results from an experiment investigating the properties of a spring.*

Mass hung on spring (g)	Force on spring (N)	Length of spring (cm)	Extension ( )
0	0	20	
100	1	22	
200	2	24	
300	3	26	
400	4	28	
500	5	30	
600	6	32	
700	7	35	
800	8	39	
900	9	43	

a) Complete the table by filling in values for *Extension* and its *units*.

b) On the axes below, plot the graph of *Extension* and *Force* for the table opposite.

c) Is the spring obeying Hooke's Law for the *straight* bits of the graph or the *curved* bits?

....

d) Between what *force values* does the spring obey Hooke's Law?

....

e) At the point where the graph starts to curve, the spring is *no longer* obeying Hooke's Law. What do we call this point?

....

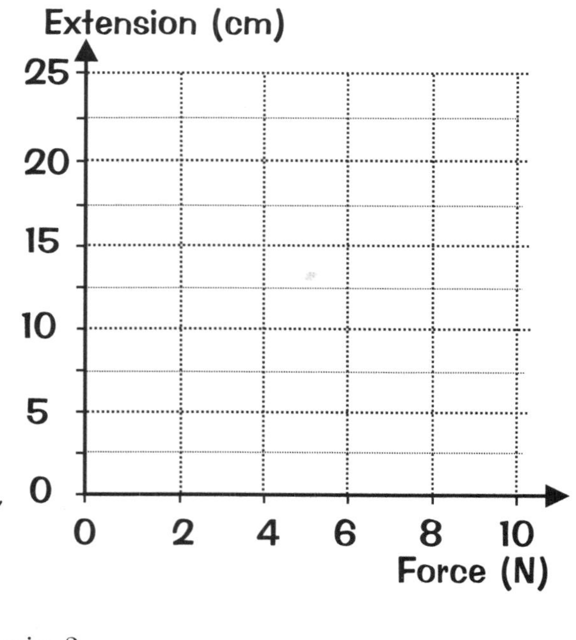

f) If a force of *less* than 5N was applied to the spring, would it return to its *original shape?*

....

What about if a force of 9N was applied to the spring? ....

g) In this case is the spring behaving *elastically* or *inelastically?* ....

Questions on Hooke's Law

Q3 Draw lines to match these *words* with their *correct descriptions*.

spring	the force being supported by something
elastic limit	the increase in length of something being stretched
plastic	an object which obeys Hooke's law
extension	the force in something being stretched
proportional	the force in something being squashed
tension	a material which stays permanently stretched
compression	loading beyond this give permanent extension
load	one quantity increases in the same way as another

Q4 *A physics class set up an experiment to investigate Hooke's law for a spring. They found that for each 100g they loaded the spring with, its length increased by 2cm.*

a) When the *load* was 2N, the *length* of the spring was 14cm. How long was it when the load was 4N? ....

b) What would its *length* be if there was *no load* hung on it?

....

c) The spring reached its *elastic limit* when it was 20cm long. What *load* was hanging on the spring at this this time? (Looking at your answer to part (a) might help).

....

d) If a load *greater* than your answer to part (c) was hung on the spring, would the spring return to its *original length* after the load was taken off? ....

Q5 Draw arrows on each of the following diagram below to show where the *forces* are acting. Also, *label* any places where there is COMPRESSION or TENSION.

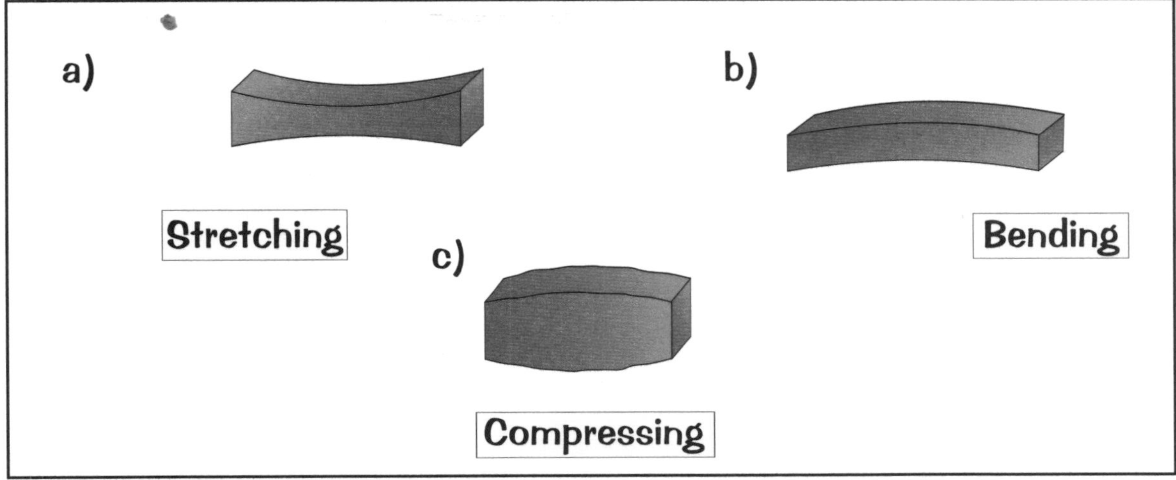

Questions on Moments

Q1 *Fill in* the gaps, using the words below. You can use each word ONCE, MORE THAN ONCE or NOT AT ALL.

force	equilibrium	bigger	anticlockwise	handle	moment	
clockwise	turn	perpendicular distance			pivot	smaller

When a force acts on an object it can do many things to it – bend it, twist it, accelerate it, etc. However, if the object has a ___________, the force makes it start to _________. This "turning force" is called a _______________. A moment is calculated from the formula:

___________ (Nm) = ________ (N) × _____________ ___________ (m)
(of the force from the pivot)

This means that the bigger the ____________ or ______________ ___________ the force is from the pivot, the ____________ the moment. Usually, we think of a moment as acting ________________ or _____________________, and if total clockwise moment equals total anticlockwise moment then the object is said to be in _______________.

Q2 *The diagram below shows two seesaws with different weights acting on them.*

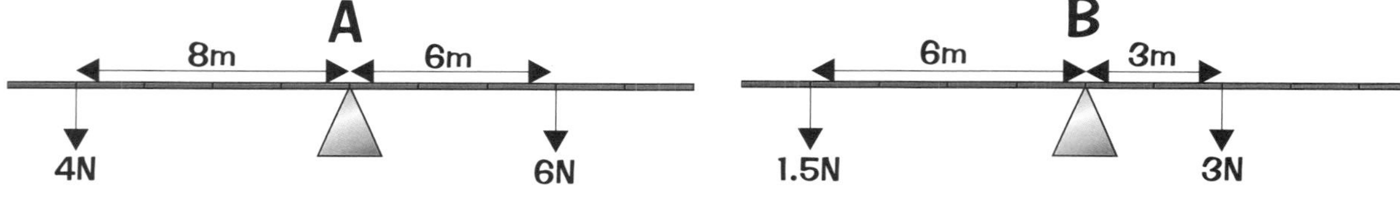

For each seesaw, calculate the *clockwise moment*, *anticlockwise moment* and say whether or not they *balance*. To calculate the moments use the formula:

Moment = Force × Perpendicular Distance

which you wrote down in the box above (and don't forget to use the correct units for your answer).

Seesaw A: Clockwise moment: ....

Anticlockwise moment: ....

Do they balance? ....

Seesaw B: Clockwise moment: ....

Anticlockwise moment: ....

Do they balance? ....

Questions on Moments

Q3 *The diagram shows a seesaw which is in equilibrium (ie balanced).* Work through parts (a) – (d) to calculate *John's mass*.

John

Lucy 30kg

1.5m 2m

a) *Lucy's weight* (remember g = 10N/kg)

Weight = _______ x _____ = ______N

b) *Lucy's moment.*

Moment = _______ x ______ = ______Nm

c) *John's moment.*

Moment = ______Nm (you don't really need to work anything out here)

d) *John's weight.*

Weight = ______/ _______ = ______N. So *John's mass* is ______/ ______ = ______kg.

Q4 *Ralph's front door hinges are a bit stiff, making the door difficult to close. The moment he needs to generate to close the door is 148.5 Nm. At first he tries to close it by pushing it 0.3m from the hinges, as shown in the diagram.*

0.3m F Door

a) Use the formula F = M/ r (where F is force) to work out the *force* he must generate to close the door.

....

Force = ... N

Ralph's smart alec friend suggests that he might find it easier if he pushed the door as far away from the hinges as possible.

0.9m New F Door

b) The door is *0.9m wide*, and Ralph pushes at this edge instead. Work out the *force* he now needs close the door.

....

Force = ... N

c) Was Ralph's friend *correct?* By how *many* newtons?

....

Q5 *Look at the diagram on the right.*

1kg

a) What is the reading on the *two* spring balances if the two readings are *equal?* ....

b) If *four* spring balances were used with the same 1 Kg block, what reading on each balance would you get if the values are again *equal?*

....

Questions on Pressure in Liquids and on Surfaces

Q1 *Complete* the passage below by filling in the gaps with the words below.

small	large	sinking	force	damage	area	high	low

Pressure is the ___________ acting on a unit ___________ of a surface. A force concentrated on a *small* area of a surface creates a __________ pressure, which can cause ___________ to the surface. For example a sharp knife and a tomato skin. However, a force spread over a ___________ area creates a ________ pressure which means little or no _______________ into the surface, like with snow shoes.

Q2 For each of these, write whether the area should be **LARGE** or **SMALL** and the pressure **HIGH** or **LOW**.

Object	Area should be: (small / large)	Pressure will be: (small / large)
A knife to cut meat		
Shoe heels that don't damage floors		
A sewing needle		
Tractor tyres for use on soft ground		
Snow skis		

Q3 *Complete* the following passage using the words in the grey box below:

1m²	1N	right angles	pascal	N/cm²	Force	newtons	Area	metres²

The formula for pressure is : Pressure = __________ / __________.

The normal unit of pressure is the ____________ (Pa), but only if the force is measured in ___________ and the area is measured in ___________________. A pressure of one Pascal (1Pa) is caused by a force of ________ acting at __________ __________ to an area of _________. For areas measured in cm^2 the unit pressure is _________ not pascals.

Q4 *Circle* the correct formula triangle for the calculation of *pressure*.

Questions on Pressure in Liquids and on Surfaces

Q5 *Using the correct formula triangle to help you answer the following questions:*

a) Work out the *pressure* exerted on the ground below by concrete slabs with area $20m^2$ and total weight of 160,000N.

....

b) What is the *pressure* the bottom of a suitcase exerts on the ground if it weighs 170N and area of the bottom is $0.1m^2$.

....

c) The same suitcase falls onto its side, the area of which is $1m^2$. What *pressure* does it excert on the ground now?

....

d) A person who has weight 800N sits down on a chair, exerting a pressure of 10000 Pa on the chair. Work out the *area* of their bottom.

....

Q6 *The diagram shows a simple hydraulic jack:*

a) Is the pressure in the liquid the *same everywhere* or *different everywhere?*

....

b) Work out the *pressure* at A?

....

....

20 N

A

Area = $100cm^2$

LOAD

B

Area = $500cm^2$

c) What must the *pressure* be at B?

....

d) Calculate what *load* can be lifted at B?

....

e) How many times greater is the *load* at B than the *effort* (force) at A?

....

f) If the load which needed to be lifted was 150N, what would the *area* at B have to be? (Hint : Write P = F/A as A = F/P and remember that pressure stays the same in the system.)

....

Questions on Pressure in Liquids and on Surfaces

Q1 *Label* this diagram of the hydraulic system in car brakes.

Use the terms:
brake fluid, tyre, brake disk, slave cylinder, brake pedal, master cylinder.

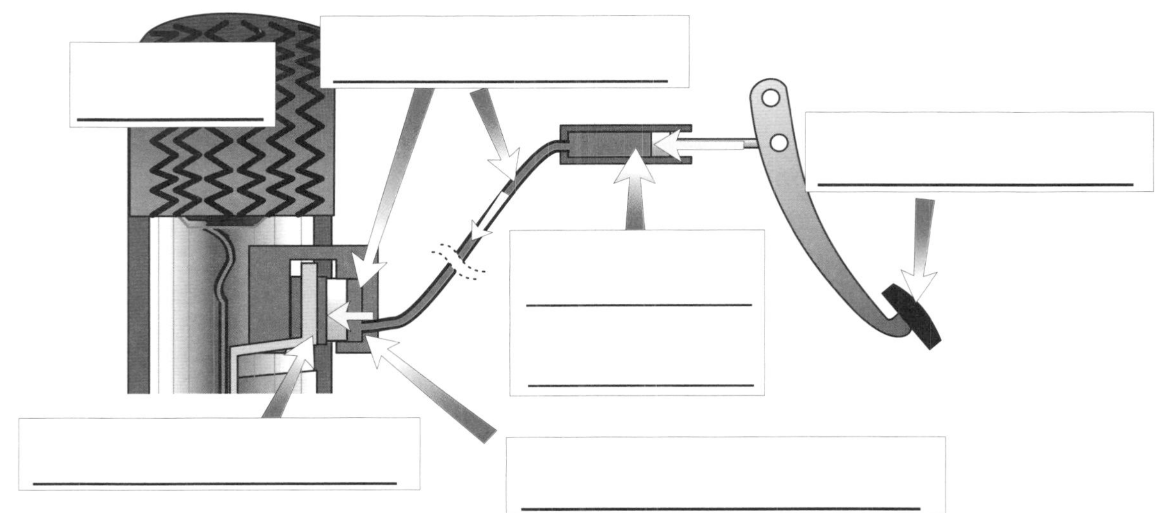

a) Which of the two cylinders in the diagram has the *larger area?*

....

b) Which of the two cylinders has the *smaller area?*

....

c) What does this mean about the *size* of the force exerted by the *brake disc* compared to that exerted by the *person* pressing on the brake?

....

d) Does the pressure of the *brake fluid* change between the master cylinder and the slave cylinder? ....

e) If the master cylinder has an area of 5cm^2 and a force of 350N is applied to the brake pedal, calculate the *pressure* in the system. (Make sure your answer has the correct units)

....

f) The slave cylinder has an area of 50cm^2. Work out the *force* it produces.

....

g) How many times the *original force* is the force produced by the slave cylinder?

....

Questions on Pressure in Liquids

Q2 *Below is a picture of Monique's fish tank and her five fish.*

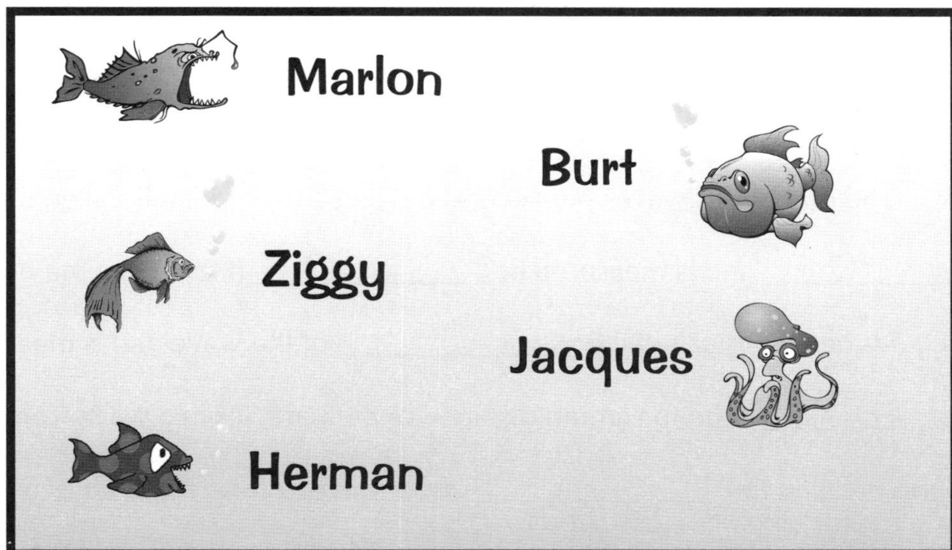

a) In which *direction(s)* does the *pressure* on each of Monique's fish act?

....

b) Would the direction(s) be *different* in different liquids? ....

c) Each of them has a *different* pressure acting on them. Write their names in *ascending* order of the pressure they are subjected to, starting with the one subject to the *lowest* pressure.

__________ __________ __________ __________ __________

Low Pressure — Medium Pressure — High Pressure

d) If the water was replaced by a *less dense* fluid, what would happen to the *pressure* on each of the fish?

....

e) What about if the water was replaced by a *more dense* liquid?

....

Q3 *Michael is pumping up his bike tyres using a small hand pump.*

a) As he pushes down the plunger on the hand pump, what happens to the *volume* of the gas inside the pump? ....

b) Does this make the pressure in the cylinder *increase* or *decrease?*

....

c) The volume of the tyre doesn't change much as he pumps air into it, but the pressure does. Does the pressure in the tyre *increase* or *decrease?*

....

Questions on the Principles of Waves

Q1 Complete the following sentences by filling in the gaps, using the words in the box.

m/sec	longitudinal	seconds	frequency	hertz	diffraction
trough	period speed	amplitude	peak	transverse	refraction

There are two different types of waves: ______________ waves and ______________ waves. The number of waves per second passing a fixed point is called the ______________ and is measured in ______________ (Hz). The time between one wave and the next is called the ______________ of the wave and is measured in ______________. The maximum distance of the particles in a wave from their resting position is called the ______________ of the wave. A highest point of a wave is called a ______________, and the lowest point of a wave is called a ______________. The distance travelled each second by a wave is called its ______________ and it is measured in ______________. Waves change their speed and wavelength when they go into different materials; this is called ______________.

Waves spread out when they pass through a small gap; this is called ______________.

Q2 *You can send a wave along a piece of string by shaking one end up and down (see diagram).*

a) What do we say the string is doing? ....

b) How would you increase: **(i)** the *frequency* and **(ii)** the *amplitude* of this wave?

(i) ....

(ii) ....

Q3 *You are floating in the sea, measuring waves (as you do). You time 5 seconds between one crest passing you and the next.*

a) What is the period of this wave?

....

b) What is the frequency of this wave?

....

Questions on the Principles of Waves

Q4 Give a definition of *wavelength*. What unit is it usually measured in?

....

Q5 *Here are six equations with frequency, wavelength and speed in them. Unfortunately some of them are wrong.*

$$\text{Speed} = \frac{\text{Frequency}}{\text{Wavelength}}$$

$$\text{Frequency} = \text{Speed} \times \text{Wavelength}$$

$$\text{Speed} = \text{Frequency} \times \text{Wavelength}$$

$$\text{Frequency} = \frac{\text{Speed}}{\text{Wavelength}}$$

$$\text{Frequency} = \frac{\text{Wavelength}}{\text{Speed}}$$

$$\text{Wavelength} = \frac{\text{Speed}}{\text{Frequency}}$$

Write down the three correct versions of the wave equation, first in words, then using the usual symbols (v for speed or velocity, f for frequency, and λ for wavelength).

....

....

....

Q6 *The diagram below shows a piece of string with a wave travelling along it.*

There are beads attached to the string in positions A, B, C, D, E, F and G.

Which bead(s) are:

a) at a crest? ....

b) at a trough? ....

c) moving up? ....

d) moving down? ....

e) not moving? ....

f) What is the amplitude of this wave? ....

g) What is the wavelength of this wave? ....

Questions on Light Waves

Q1 *The diagram below shows a lamp giving out light, making the doll cast a shadow.*

Using some of the words from the word box, complete the following sentences.

luminous	open	transparent	reflects	light	opaque	white	straight	absorbs

a) Something that gives out its own light, like the lamp, is said to be ....

Lamp

Doll

b) The doll does not give out light, but we see it because it .... light.

c) A *shadow* is an area where .... does not reach. To make a shadow you need an object which will stop the light (an .... object).

Light *cannot bend* around the object because light travels in .... lines.

Q2 *Visible light is light which we can see with our eyes. Sunlight contains visible light.*

a) Looking at a rainbow tells us a very simple thing about sunlight. What is this?

....

b) What is the name for the triangular-shaped glass block that can be used to make a "rainbow" in the laboratory? ....

Q3 The table below compares some properties of *red* light waves and *violet* light waves.

Use the words from the word box to complete the table.

Wave Property	Red Light	Violet Light
Speed		
Frequency		
Wavelength		

long
low
same
high
short

Q4 *The colours in a rainbow are always in the same order.*

a) What is the correct order of the colours in the visible spectrum?

....

b) Describe an easy way to remember the order of these colours.

....

....

Questions on Light Waves

Q5 *The diagram shows a ray of white light entering a glass prism.*

Draw the path of the light as it passes through. Label the colours of the light leaving the prism.

White Light

Glass Prism

Q6 *Green is in the middle of the spectrum.*
Read each of the sentences below and for each one, decide if it true or false. Then put a tick in the relevant boxes.

	TRUE	FALSE
a) ***Green light has a longer wavelength than yellow light.***	☐	☐
b) ***Red light has a lower frequency than blue light.***	☐	☐
c) ***Increasing the frequency of green light could turn it blue.***	☐	☐
d) ***Yellow light travels more slowly than violet light.***	☐	☐
e) ***Orange light has a higher frequency than red light.***	☐	☐

Q7 *Waves A, B and C below represent red, green and violet light waves (not in that order).*

Read the sentences below and write down the letters of the ones you think are correct.

A

B

C

a) "B" *is violet.*

b) *The red light has the largest amplitude.*

c) "C" *has the highest frequency.*

d) Green *has the smallest amplitude.*

e) "A" *has the shortest wavelength.*

....

Q8 *I was walking home recently on a very misty night. As a car went past, its headlights cast my shadow in mid-air.*

a) What's unusual about something like this happening?

....

b) Why did it happen on that particular night?

....

....

Questions on Sound Waves

Q1 a) What causes a sound wave to be created?

....

b) What *vibrates* in the following objects to create a sound?

c) What carries the vibration from an object to your ear?

....

Q2 *The diagram below shows a sound wave in air. It is travelling away from a loudspeaker.*

a) Complete the missing words in the diagram.

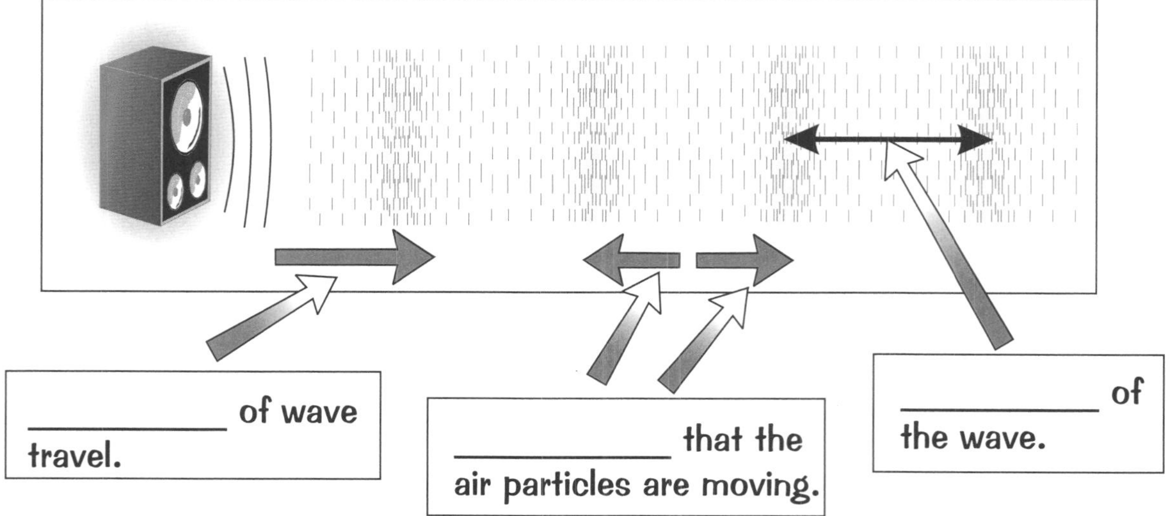

b) Is the sound wave a *transverse* or a *longitudinal* wave? ....

Q3 a) Which of the following can sound travel through? Mark them with a tick.

☐ ***SOLIDS*** ☐ ***A VACUUM*** ☐ ***LIQUIDS*** ☐ ***GASES***

b) Which medium in a) does sound generally travel the fastest in? ....

Questions on Sound Waves

Q4 *The diagram below shows an alarm clock ringing inside an airtight bell jar. The air is sucked out using a vacuum pump.*

a) What happens to the *sound* of the alarm clock as the air is gradually pumped out? ....

b) What does this result tell you about sound?

....

c) Why do you think the clock needs to sit on a foam block?

....

Q5 *Six frequencies are listed below.*

2Hz, 20Hz, 200Hz, 2000Hz, 2kHz, 20kHz

a) Which two frequencies are the same? ....

b) Which one is the lowest frequency humans can hear? ....

c) For which one could you easily count the vibrations without instruments? ....

d) Which is closest to the highest frequency humans can hear? ....

Q6 Using some of the words from the word box, complete the paragraph below. You don't have to use all of the words — some may be left over.

lower higher difficult loud highest older quieter

As people get ________ the frequency of the ________ sound that they can hear gets ________. This makes it ________ to understand what is being said. This damage happens much more quickly if people are regularly exposed to ________ sounds.

Q7 Complete the sentences a) to c) below:

a) Noise is unwanted .... and can be a form of pollution in the environment.

b) Levels of noise are measured in ....

c) Materials which .... noise are called sound insulation and include carpets, curtains and .... glazing.

Questions on Pitch and Loudness

Q1 *In the following questions, use words from the word box to fill in the blanks. You won't need all of the words in the box.*

WORD LIST
vacuum
vibration
wave
wavelength
amplitude
frequency
330
300 000 000
solid
gas
period

a) Sound is a type of .... motion.

b) To make a sound wave there must be a ....

c) Sound waves travel at about .... m/s in air.

d) The distance between identical points on waves next to each other is called the ....

e) The number of vibrations per second is called the ....

f) The maximum distance of particles from their resting positions is called the .... of the wave.

g) Sound cannot travel through a ....

Q2 *Anna strikes a tuning fork and makes a high but quiet sound.*

a) What are the prongs of the tuning fork doing?

....

b) *The tuning fork is dipped into a cup of water after it has been struck.* Describe how the water will move.

....

....

c) If a tuning fork with longer prongs is struck, what difference in the sound would you hear?

....

Q3 *Changing the frequency or amplitude of a sound wave affects the type of sound you hear.* Complete the following sentences by ringing the correct words in the brackets.

"Increasing the [**frequency / amplitude**] of a sound will [**increase / decrease**] the pitch of the sound and a [**higher / lower**] note will be heard. Decreasing the [**frequency / amplitude**] will [**increase / decrease**] the pitch of the sound.
Increasing the amplitude will increase the [**pitch / loudness**] of the sound and decreasing the amplitude will make the sound [**louder / quieter / higher / lower**]."

Questions on Pitch and Loudness

Q4 *An oscilloscope is used to shows the shapes of electrical signals.*

What can you use to turn a sound signal into an electrical signal?

....

Q5 *A tuning fork is used to produce a single pure note. This sound is made into an electrical signal and displayed on an oscilloscope.*

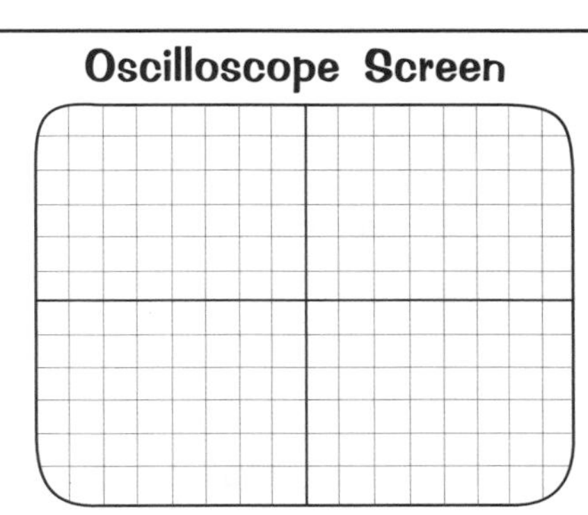

a) Draw on the screen opposite the shape of the wave you would expect to see.

b) Describe the shape of the trace you would get if the note was not a pure note, e.g. someone talking.

....

....

Q6 *Kerry is investigating sounds of different frequency, using an oscilloscope, a microphone, a signal generator and a loudspeaker. She uses the signal generator and the loudspeaker to create sounds of different amplitudes and frequencies, and connects the microphone to the oscilloscope.*

She records in her table:

1. A drawing of the signal on the oscilloscope screen.
2. The frequency (in Hz).
3. The amplitude (in volts).
4. And the loudness and pitch of the sound.

Drawing of Trace	Frequency (Hz)	Amplitude (V)	Sound heard
+4 +2 0 -2 -4	10 000	2V	High and Quiet
+4 +2 0 -2 -4	15 000	4V	
+4 +2 0 -2 -4	20 000	2V	
+4 +2 0 -2 -4	25 000	2V	

a) Complete the table with the results you would expect her to find. She's already done one line. Make sure you mention the pitch and volume for each sound. Be careful — this is trickier than it looks.

b) Why is it difficult for us to be certain if she would hear anything at 20,000Hz?

....

....

Questions on Ultrasound

Ultrasound is sound with a higher frequency than we can hear.

Q1 *A signal generator can be used with a loudspeaker and amplifier to make sounds of a large frequency range (as in the diagram opposite). An oscilloscope displays the traces for these sounds.*

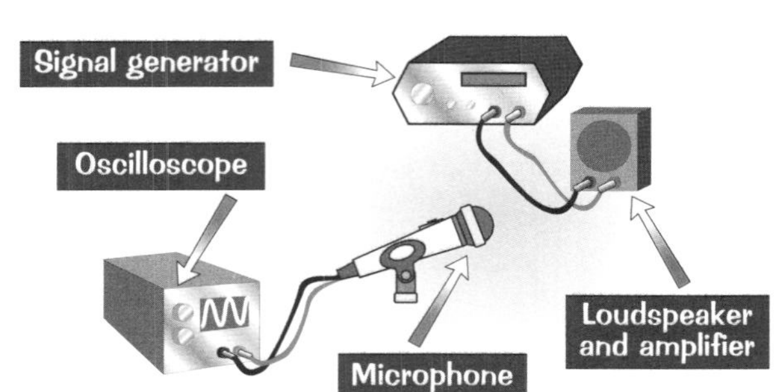

Match each of the apparatus on the left, with its what it does from the list on the right.

APPARATUS	PURPOSE
Signal Generator	Shows a visual display of an electrical signal
Loudspeaker	Turns electricity into a sound wave
Microphone	Produces oscillating electricity
Oscilloscope	Turns sound waves into electricity

Q2 Complete the following sentences about Ultrasound, using words from the word box. You don't have to use them all.

ultrasound amplitude quiet generator amplifier microphone signal frequency
Sounds above 20 000Hz have too high a ________________ to be heard by the human ear. Such sounds can be made using a ____________-____________, ________________ and a loudspeaker. Sounds with frequencies above the "hearing threshold" are called ________________.

Q3 Calculate the *wavelengths* of the ultrasonic frequencies in a), b), & c) (in air).
— Take the speed of sound in air to be 330m/s, and watch out for your units.

a) 25kHz ....

b) 30kHz ....

c) 100kHz ....

d) Why is it important to state that the sounds are travelling through air?

....

Questions on Ultrasound

Q4 What frequency will a sound wave in air have if its wavelength is 0.5cm?

....

Q5 *Bats use ultrasound to catch their prey, and can "see" with it.*

a) However, a bat using ultrasound is a bit like me using a torch on the way home at night, rather than looking around in the daytime. Why is this?

....

A bat can not "see" anything smaller than the wavelength of the ultrasound it sends out. Last week, I saw a bat catch a moth that was about 1cm wide.

b) What can you say about the wavelength of the ultrasound the bat needs to send out to be able to "see" the moth? ....

c) Give another example of a place where ultrasound can be used to "see" things.

....

Q6 *You should be able to describe several of the different applications of ultrasound.*

Listed below are six applications for ultrasound. For each, draw arrows to match it with the correct boxes. (The first one is done for you).

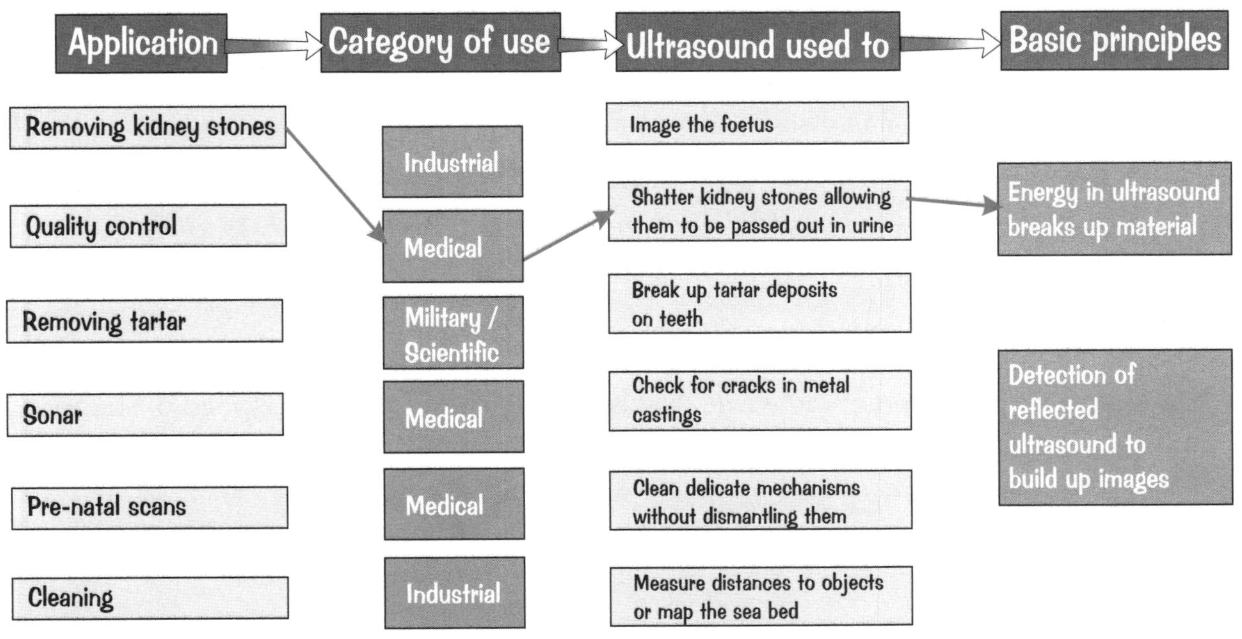

Questions on The Speed of Sound

Questions about making distance measurements using reflected sound are very popular in exams. So it's worth learning this stuff carefully.

Q1 a) What is the speed of sound in air in metres per second? ....

b) How is the speed of sound different in water compared to air?

....

Q2 A group of students has been sent outside to carry out an experiment to estimate the speed of sound. One student bangs two wooden blocks together. Two other students measure the time between the bang and hearing the sound echo from a large wall, 200m away. They repeat the experiment until they have ten measurements for the time. These times are shown in the table.

Time Interval (s)				
1.11	1.23	1.29	1.17	1.15
1.19	1.21	1.13	1.27	1.25

a) Calculate the average of these times.

....

b) How far did the sound travel during this time? ....

c) Write down the formula you need to use for working out the speed of the sound.

....

d) Calculate the speed of sound in this experiment.

....

Q3 *Sound is a wave and there are two equations for calculating the speed of a wave. In an experiment it took a sound (of frequency 10 kHz) a time of 0.0004s to travel along a 1m steel bar and return.*

a) How far has the sound wave travelled? ....

b) Calculate the speed of the wave. Is this faster or slower than the speed of sound in air?

....

c) Use the equation: wavelength = speed ÷ frequency to work out the wavelength.

....

Questions on The Speed of Sound

Q4 *Another group of students try a different way of measuring the speed of sound.*

The students are spread out at 200m intervals across a field, each has a stopwatch. The student with the starting pistol presses the trigger and drops his arm at the same. All the students start their stop watches when the arm drops and stop them when they hear the sound.

These are their results :

Distance (m)	200	400	600	800	1 000
Time (s)	0.9	1.2	1.8	2.4	3.0

a) Plot a graph of the results on the axes below, and draw a best fit straight line through them.

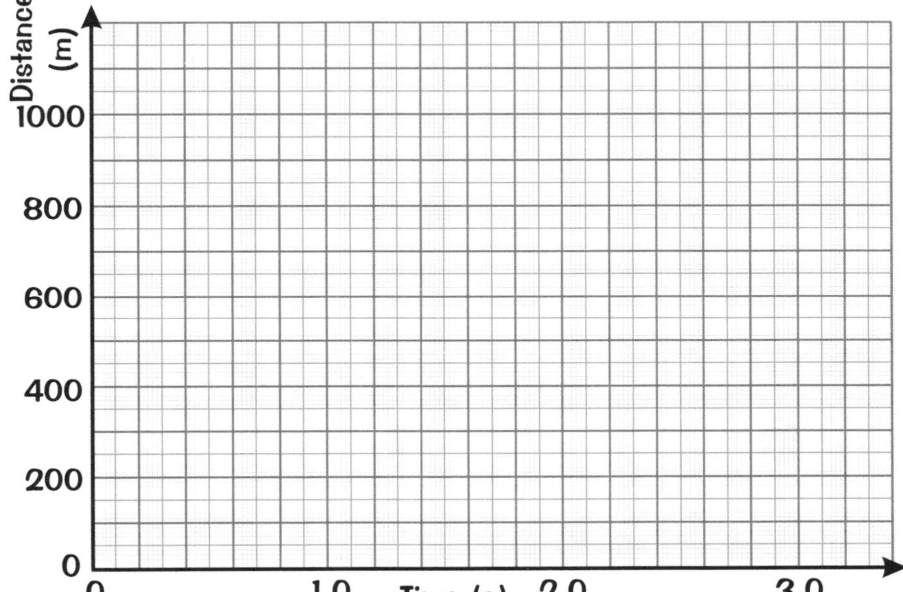

b) Which point does not quite fit the pattern?

....

c) Work out the speed of sound from this experiment. ....

....

Q5 *A small submarine is using* <u>*sonar*</u> *to locate objects in murky water. The submarine sends out a pulse and receives three echoes back. The table below shows the time for these echoes.*

Echo	1	2	3
Time (s)	0.2	0.4	0.1
Distance (m)			

Complete the table by calculating the distance of each object from the submarine. (The speed of sound in water is 1500m/s.)

Questions on Reflection

Q1 *Like sound, light can be reflected off surfaces. In the following questions, fill the gaps using the words from the word box.*

dull	incidence	reflection	clear	shiny	reflect	diffuse	ray	normal	equal

a) Some objects give out their own light. All other objects we see because they .... light.

b) Some objects reflect light without disrupting it. This is called a .... reflection and objects which do this look ....

c) Most objects disrupt the reflected light giving a .... reflection. These objects look ....

d) The name for a thin beam of light which can be used to study reflection is a ....

e) The line drawn at right angles to a mirror's surface is called the ....

f) The law of reflection states that the angle of .... is .... to the angle of ....

Q2 The diagrams 1, 2 and 3 shows rays arriving at a surface.

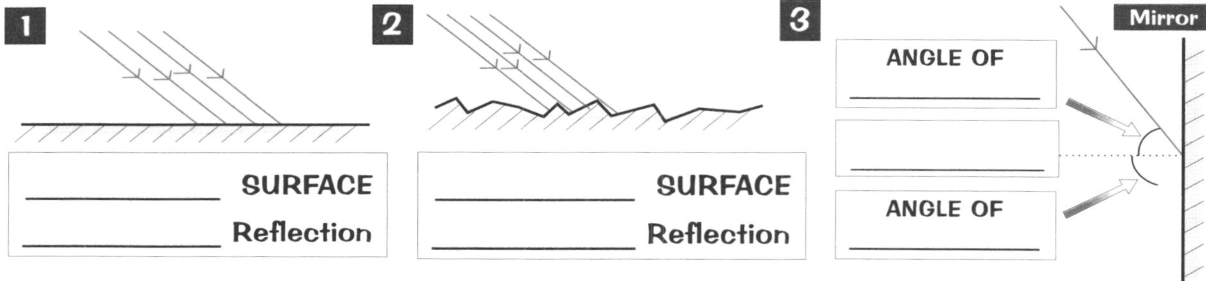

For each diagram, complete the labels and draw the reflected rays.

Q3 The picture opposite shows two people sitting on a bench, looking at the reflections of statues in the window.

Which of the statues can each person see?

(Draw rays on the diagram if it helps)

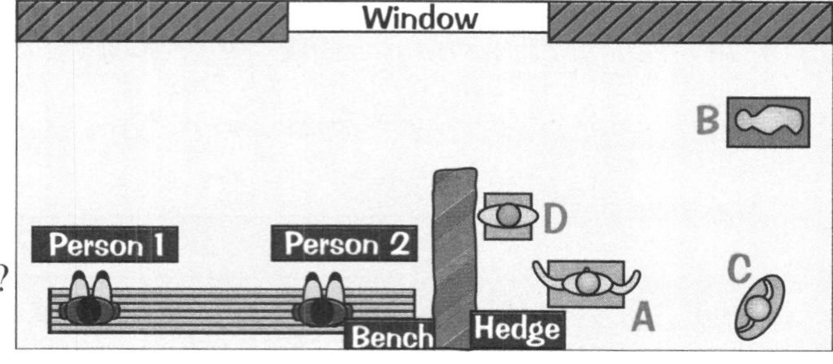

Person 1 ....

Person 2 ....

Questions on Refraction

Q1 Fill the gaps in the sentences about *refraction*, using words from the grey box. Some of the words may not be needed.

direction	decrease	slowly	edge	middle
vacuum	quickly	perspex	increase	water	speeds

a) Light travels at different .... in different materials.

b) Light travels more .... in glass than in air.

c) When a light rays travels from air into glass, its speed will ....

d) When the light travels from glass into air, its speed will ....

e) The change in the speed and .... happens at the .... of the glass block.

f) Other materials where light will travel more slowly than in air include .... and ....

Q2 Look at Diagrams 1 and 2 below. One shows a ray travelling from air to glass and the other shows a ray travelling from glass to air. Complete sentences (a) and (b) by filling in the letter of the correct ray.

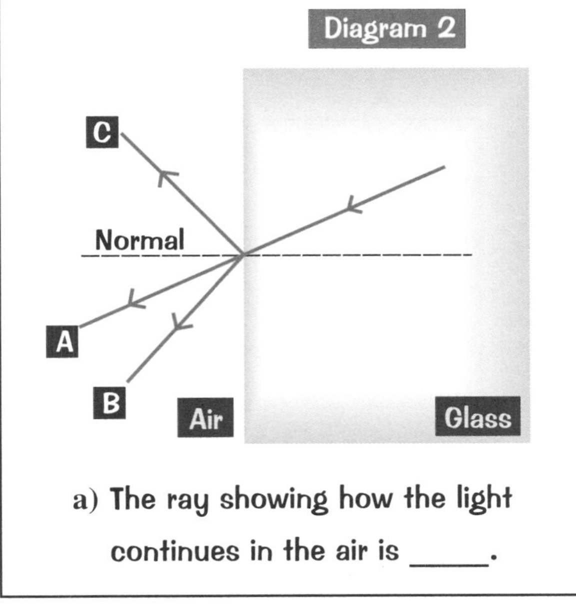

a) The ray showing how the light continues in the air is _____.

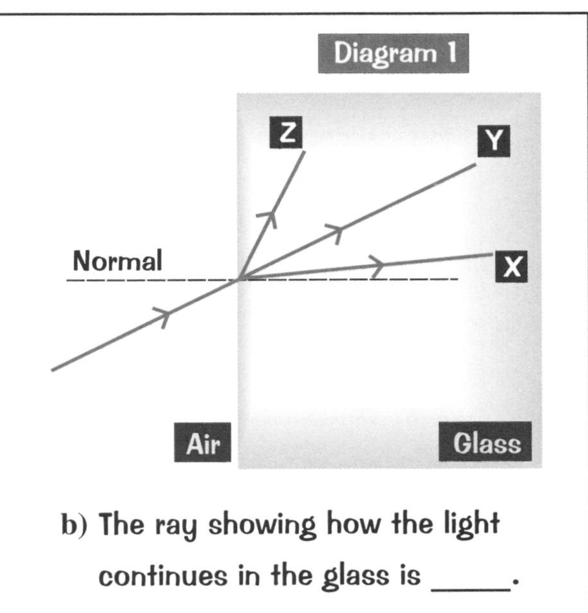

b) The ray showing how the light continues in the glass is _____.

Q3 *Fill the gaps in this statement, summarising the refraction of light in a glass block.*

When a ray of light enters a glass block it is bent .... the normal, but when a ray of light leaves the glass block it is bent .... the normal.

Questions on Special Cases of Refraction

Q1 *The diagram opposite shows a light ray entering a glass <u>prism</u>.*

a) Mark on the diagram (with a cross) the place where the ray enters the prism.

b) Draw the normal to the face (side) at the point where the ray enters the prism.

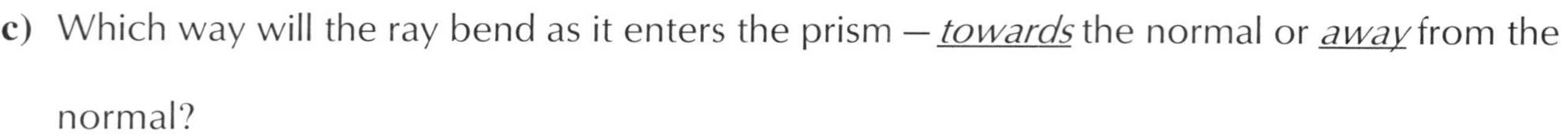

c) Which way will the ray bend as it enters the prism — *<u>towards</u>* the normal or *<u>away</u>* from the normal? ....

d) Draw the path of the ray inside the prism. Continue it to the other side.

e) Draw the normal to the face at the point where the ray leaves the prism.

f) Which way will the ray bend as it leaves the prism? ....

g) Now draw the ray outside the prism.

Q2 *The diagram below shows a light ray entering at right angles to a <u>semi-circular</u> glass block.*

a) Draw the normal to the block where the ray enters.

b) What do you notice about the direction of the normal and the direction of the ray?

....

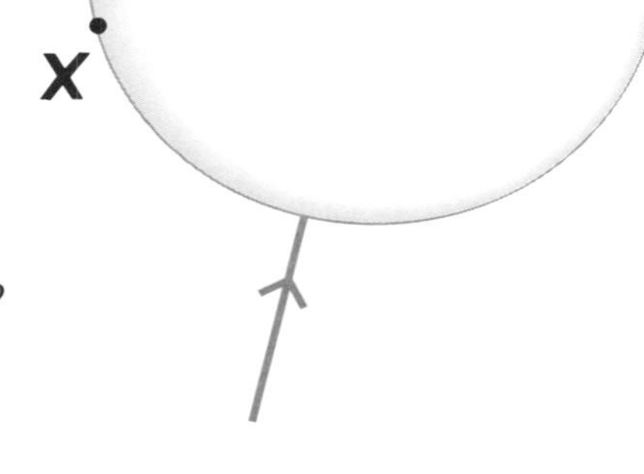

c) Does the ray change direction when it enters the block?

Why is this unusual?

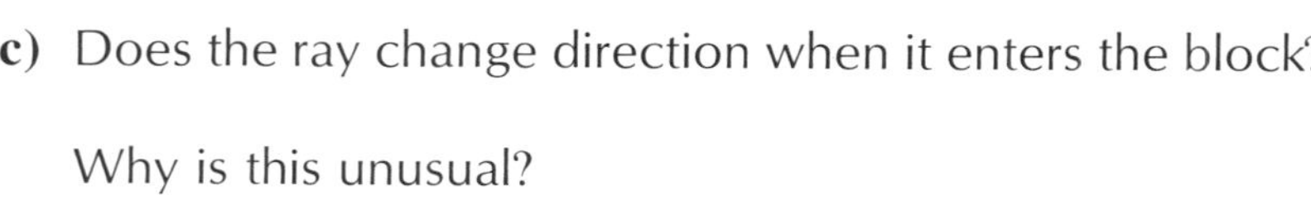

....

....

d) Draw the path of the ray inside the block. Continue it to the other side.

e) Draw the normal to the face where the ray leaves the block, and the ray leaving the block.

f) *If the ray had entered the block at point X (again, at right angles to the surface of the block), something different would have happened.*

Draw on the diagram the path for this light ray.

Questions on Total Internal Reflection

Q1 Complete this paragraph about *total internal reflection* by putting a ring around the correct answer in each pair of words.

"Total internal reflection occurs when light is travelling in a material like [**glass / metal**] and comes to the [**edge / middle**] of the block. If the light meets the boundary at a large angle to the [**incident ray / normal**], the ray is [**refracted / diffracted / reflected**], not [**refracted / reflected**]. The angle at which internal reflection begins is called the [**critical / incident / normal**] angle and is about [**22 / 42 / 90**] degrees in glass."

Q2 *The diagram below shows two identical glass blocks, BLOCK 1 and BLOCK 2.*

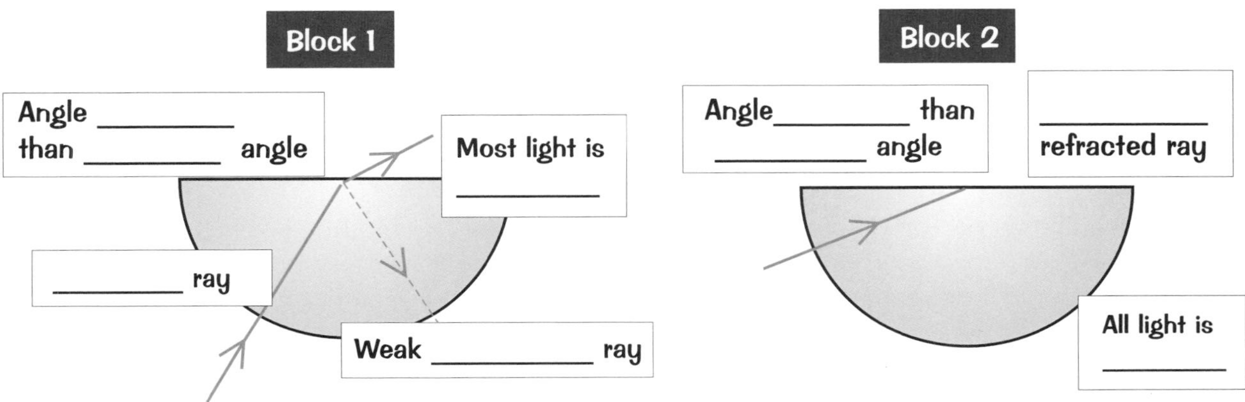

a) Complete the labelling for BLOCK 1.

b) For BLOCK 2, draw the reflected ray inside the block and then complete the labelling.

Q3 Label this diagram of an optical fibre using words from the word box .

total internal reflection	light ray	inner core	plastic sheath	outer layer

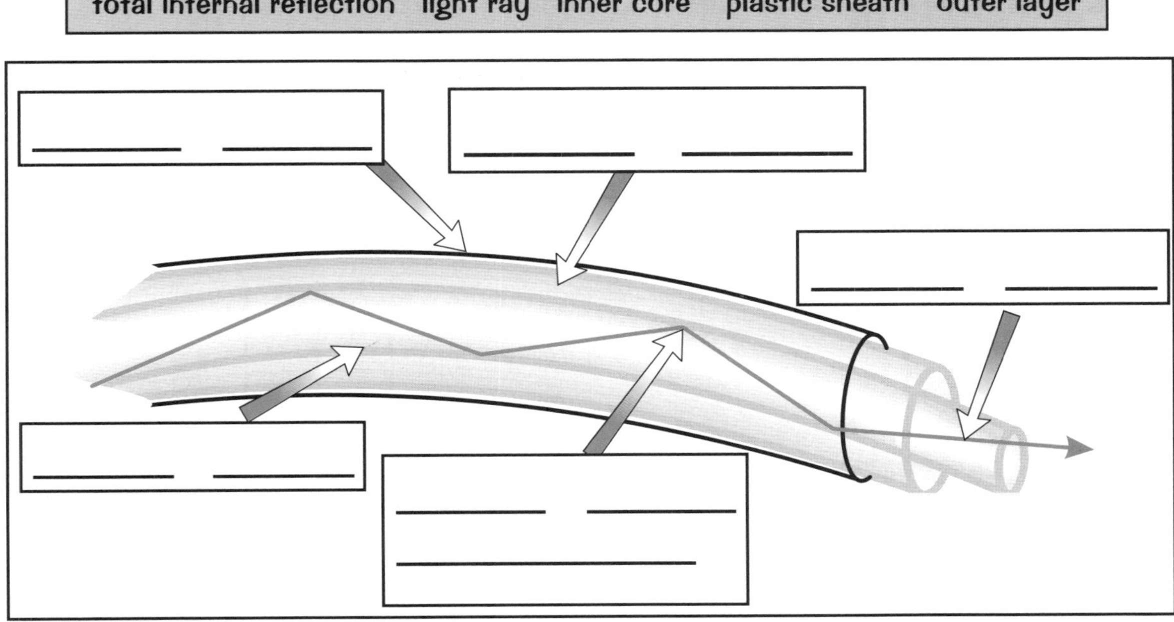

Questions on Diffraction

Q1 Use the words from the word box below, to fill the gaps in the paragraph. (You may not need all of the words listed here).

wavelength	narrower	refraction	open	semicircular
gap obstacle	bend	reflection	amplitude	diffraction

Waves will ______________ when they go through a ______________ or past an ______________. This effect is called ______________.

The ______________ the gap, the more diffraction there is. If the gap is about the same size as the ______________ of the wave, ______________ shaped waves will be produced.

Q2 *The following diagrams a) to d) show plane waves approaching obstacles. (You may have seen this demonstrated in a ripple tank).*

Draw waves on the diagrams to show what happens when they pass the various obstacles.

a) Diffraction at a wide gap

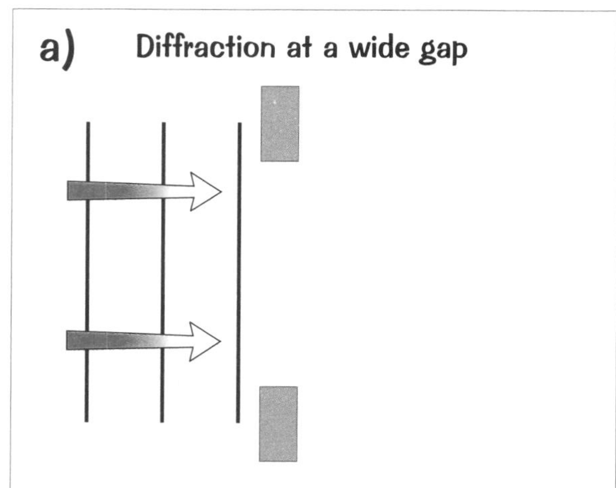

b) Diffraction at a narrow gap

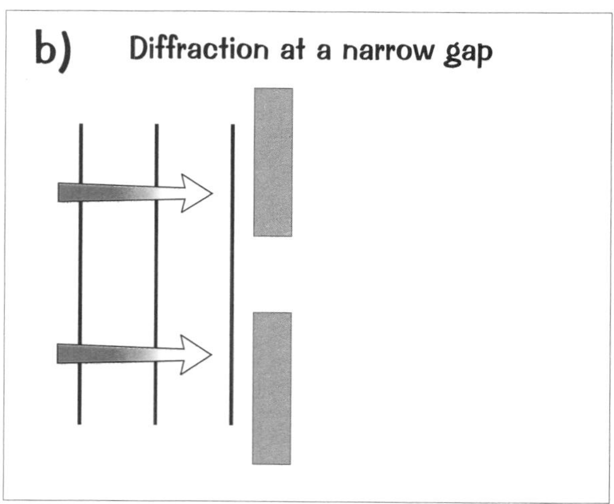

c) Diffraction at an edge

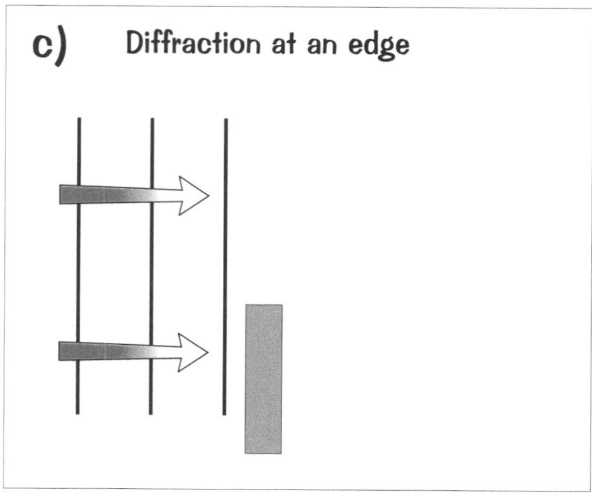

d) Diffraction round an object

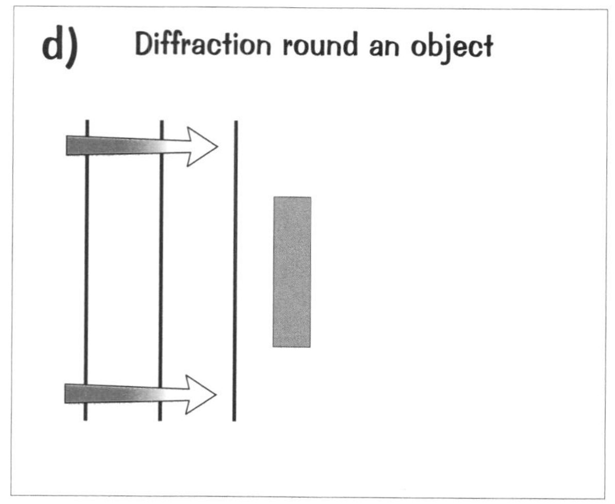

Questions on Diffraction

Q3 *This diagram shows an experiment to demonstrate the diffraction of light. The laser shines red light through a narrow slit and the light shows up on a white screen.*

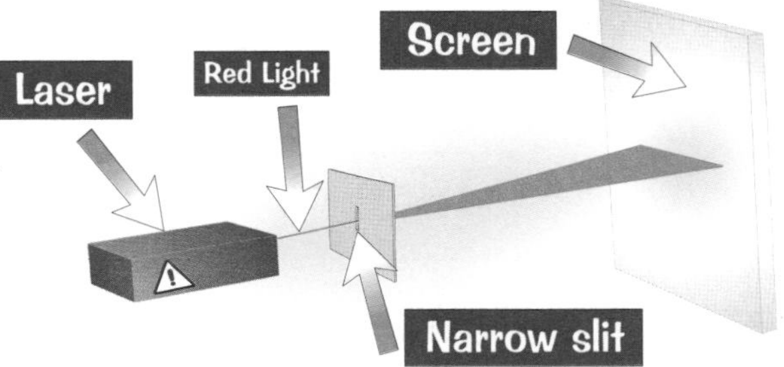

a) Why does the slit have to be very narrow?

b) What would happen to the pattern if you made the slit narrower?

c) What would happen if you made it wider?

d) What would happen if you used green light instead of red light?

Q4 How will the wavelength of a radio wave and the size of an obstacle have to compare if the wave is to bend (diffract) around the obstacle?

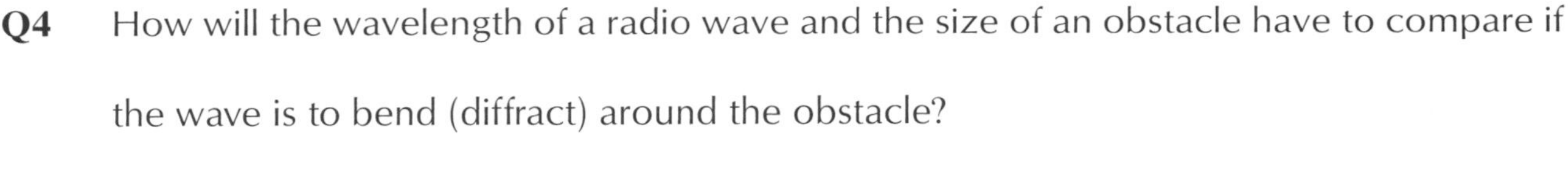

Q5 The diagrams below show shortwave TV waves and longwave radio waves near a hill.

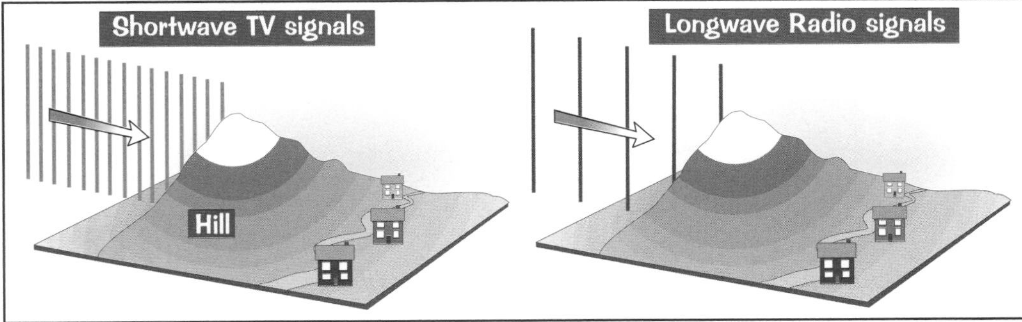

a) Draw on the diagrams how the wave patterns change as the waves pass the hills.

b) Suggest a reason why people in the houses in the picture could listen to the cricket match on Longwave Radio 4 but not be able to watch it on the television.

Questions on Optical Instruments

Optical instruments all rely upon basic principles which you should know inside out.

Q1 Complete the following sentences by circling the correct answers in the pairs of words.

When light rays travel from *air* into *glass* they bend [**away from / towards**] the normal.

When a ray of light travels from *glass* into *air* it bends [**away from / towards**] the normal.

Q2 The diagram below show a Single Lens Reflex (SLR) camera, popular with photographers.

a) What part of the camera focuses the light?

....

b) What part of the camera records the image?

....

c) What part of the camera controls the amount of light entering the camera?

....

d) What part of the camera has to move to allow a picture to be taken?

....

e) What type of reflection is occurring inside the pentaprism?

....

The diagram opposite shows a standard pair of binoculars.

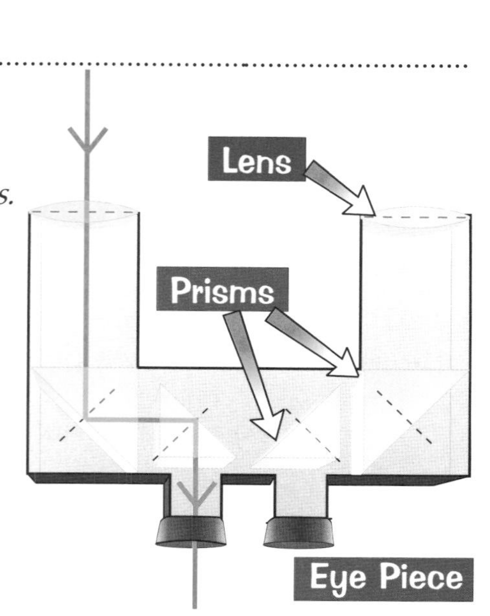

Q3 What is happening in the prisms in a pair of binoculars?

....

Q4 Draw the path of the light ray for the right hand side of the binoculars.

Questions on Optical Instruments

Q5 *The diagram opposite shows light entering a* *periscope**. The coloured line represents a light ray entering the periscope.*

a) Where (A, B, C or D) would you put your eye to use the periscope? ....

b) Draw the light path through the periscope.

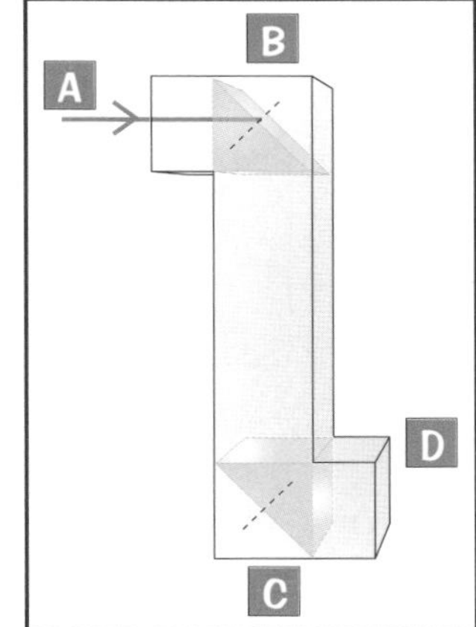

Q6 *Periscopes are used in many different situations.*

Give two examples where you might use a periscope.

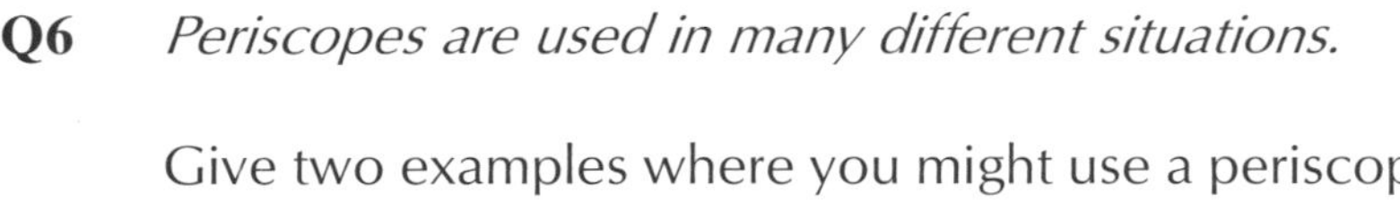

.... , ...

Q7 *This diagram shows a mirror periscope that has been put together incorrectly.*

a) On the diagram draw the paths of two light rays travelling to the eye — one from the top of the tree and one from the trunk.

b) What will be wrong with the image from this periscope? ....

c) In the blank box to the right redraw the periscope so that it works correctly. Also mark in the source and the eye.

d) Draw the light paths in your picture from part **c)**.

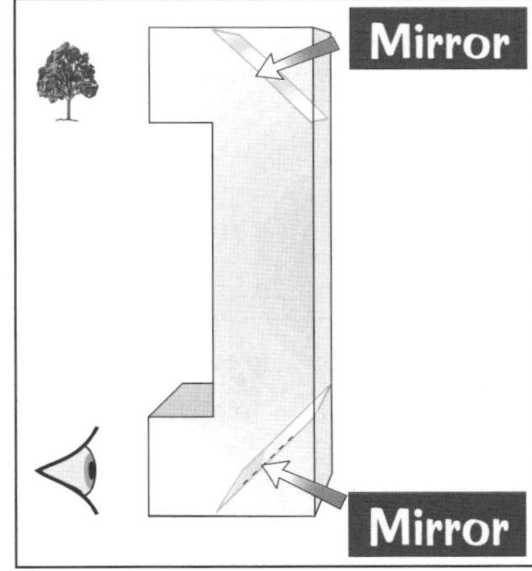

Q8 *The diagram below shows a light ray being reflected by a* *bicycle reflector**.*

a) Why doesn't the light ray change direction (refract) at A, as it goes from the air into the plastic?

....

....

b) At which letters does total internal reflection occur?

....

c) Draw the path of the light from after it has reached C.

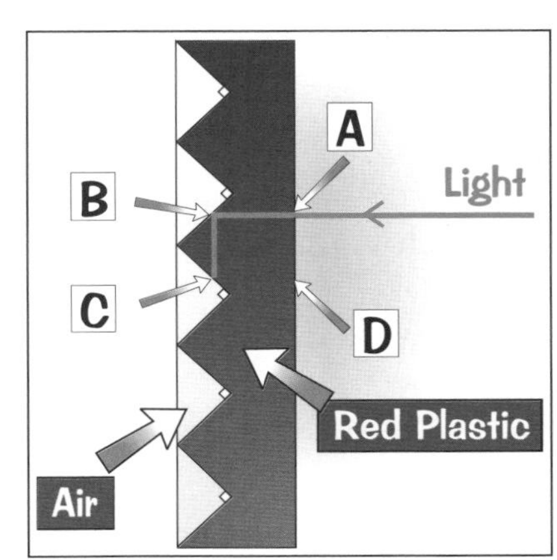

Questions on the Electromagnetic Spectrum

Q1 Complete the following sentences using words from the word box below. You may use the words once, more than once, or not at all.

speed radio waves electromagnetic gamma two seven vacuum rays X-ray infra visible red frequency light shortest ultraviolet microwave spectrum wavelength medium longest

a) *Electromagnetic* (EM) waves form a continuous ....

b) For a given .... all EM waves travel with roughly the same ....

In a .... this is about 3 x 10^8 m/s.

c) For convenience, we classify EM waves into .... types.

d) The correct order for these types of EM wave is (beginning with longest wavelength):

....

....

e) .... waves have the lowest frequency and the .... wavelength,

and .... have the highest frequency and the .... wavelength.

f) Our eyes are sensitive to EM waves from the .... spectrum only.

Q2 *Match the types of radiation (left) with its correct wavelength (right). The first one is done for you.*

Radiation	Wavelength
Visible Light	10^{-5} m (0.01 mm)
Radiowaves	10^{-7} m
Infrared	10^{-2} m (1 cm)
Gamma Rays	10^{-10} m
Microwaves	10^{-8} m
Ultraviolet	10^{0} m (1 m)
X- Rays	10^{-12} m

Q3 How many times longer is a typical visible light wave compared with an X-ray wave?

....

Q4 What is the speed of any electromagnetic wave, travelling in space (a vacuum)?

....

Questions on the Electromagnetic Spectrum

Q5 Match the "Types of Radiation" (left) with its "Effects on Living Tissue" and its "Use". (Use a ruler to draw the lines). The first one is done for you.

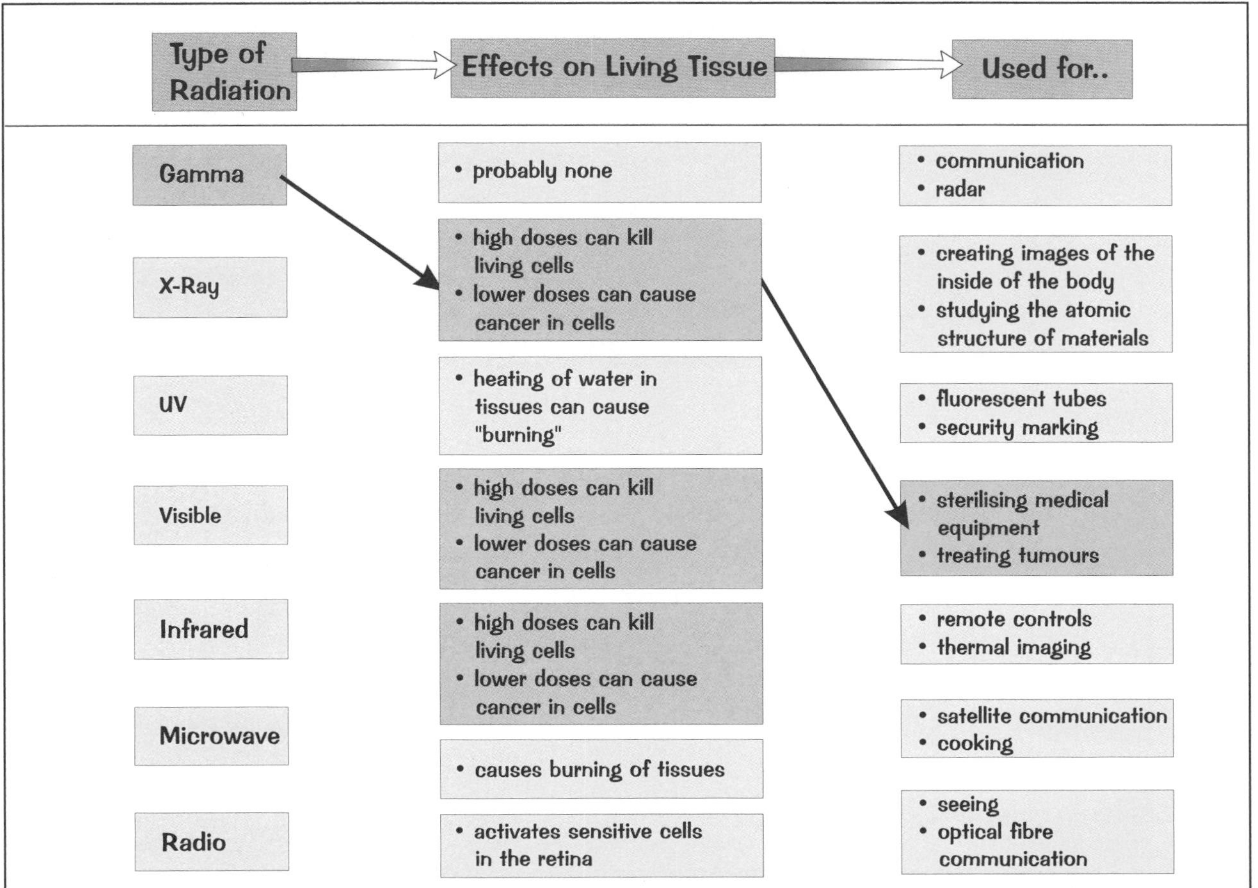

Q6 a) What colours of light would you expect to see at positions X and Y in the diagram?

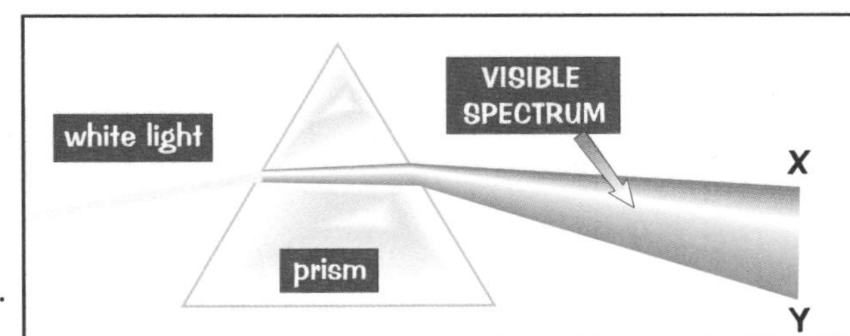

X: ....

Y: ....

b) Write down IN ORDER, all the colours you would see starting with X and finishing with Y.

....

c) What is this "light splitting" effect called?

....

d) A rainbow is created in a similar way. What is acting as the prism in this case?

....

Questions on the Solar System

Q1 The statements below are about the Solar System. Decide for each whether they are *true* or *false*, and tick the appropriate box.

True	False		
☐	☐	**a)**	There are nine planets in the Solar System.
☐	☐	**b)**	The Sun makes its energy by changing hydrogen gas into water.
☐	☐	**c)**	Mercury is the outermost planet.
☐	☐	**d)**	The Sun is the most massive object in the solar system.
☐	☐	**e)**	The planets all orbit around the Sun.
☐	☐	**f)**	We see the planets because they make their own light.
☐	☐	**g)**	Stars in other solar systems look dim because they are smaller than the Sun.

Q2 The diagram below shows the *outer planets* of the Solar System.

a) One planet's name has been left out. *Fill in* the missing name in the diagram.

b) One planet has been *missed* from the diagram altogether. *Which* planet is missing, and between which two planets does it orbit? ....

....

Questions on the Solar System

Q3 *Jupiter and the Sun are both members of the Solar System. The Sun is a star, but Jupiter is a planet. Below are a number of facts about the Sun and Jupiter.*

For each fact, decide whether it is a valid reason for the Sun being called a *star* or Jupiter being called a *planet*. If you think it is a valid reason, tick the box next to it.

- ☐ **a)** The atmosphere around Jupiter contains hydrogen and helium.
- ☐ **b)** We see the Sun and Jupiter at different times.
- ☐ **c)** The Sun generates energy by nuclear fusion.
- ☐ **d)** Objects orbit around the Sun.
- ☐ **e)** Jupiter rotates rapidly.
- ☐ **f)** The Sun gives off its own light, but we see Jupiter only by reflected sunlight.

Jupiter

Sun

Q4 Suppose we give all the planets numbers, according to their distance from the Sun; e.g. Mercury = 1, Venus = 2, etc. (Do not include the asteroid belt in your calculations).

What are the answers to the following?

a) The number of Mercury + the number of Earth. ....

b) The number of Mars + the number of Jupiter. ....

c) The number of Venus × the number of Saturn. ....

d) The number of Uranus – the number of Earth. ....

e) The number of Venus + the number of Neptune. ....

f) The number of Pluto / the number of Earth. ....

g) The number of Saturn – the number of Mercury. ....

Q5 In a similar sort of way, if you had a spacecraft that could travel between planets, where would you end up in the following cases?

a) Start at Mercury and go outwards 2 planets. ....

b) Start at Neptune and go inwards 3 planets. ....

c) Start at Mars and go outwards 1 planet. ....

d) Start at the Earth and go outwards 4 planets. ....

e) Start at Pluto and go inwards 3 planets. ....

f) Start at Venus and go inwards 2 (a bit tricky). ....

Questions on the Planets

Q1 *A science fiction series is being planned by a TV company. For the series the authors have come up with some information about five planets orbiting a star. The name of the star in the series is Grull.*

Data about the planets of Grull are given in the table below.

Name of planet	Distance from Grull (millions of km)	Surface	Atmosphere
Umblem	50	Rocky	None
Afton	100	Rocky	Thick CO_2
Sedash	150	Rocky	Thick N_2 and O_2
Clunoc	250	Rocky	Thin CO_2
Glabwell	778	Gaseous	Thick methane and ammonia

Sedash is the planet most similar to the Earth.

a) Which of the planets in the series is most similar to *Jupiter?* ....

b) Which planet is most similar to *Venus?* ....

The writers are planning an episode in which a spaceship travels from Afton to Umblem. One writer says that the surface temperature on Afton will be higher than that on Umblem. Another disagrees.

c) Compare the Grull system to our Solar System. Would you expect Afton to be *hotter* or *colder* than Umblem? ....

d) What might be the cause of Umblem having *no atmosphere?*

....

....

Q2 *Here are a number of mixed up planets from our solar system, and some facts.*

Unscramble the planets' names, and match them up with the facts by drawing an arrow from the planet to the correct fact.

Scrambled Planet	Unscrambled Planet	Fact
a) TOUPL		Only planet mainly covered in water
b) REYRMUC		Planet furthest from the Sun
c) RATHE		Biggest planet in the Solar System
d) RUNTAS		Planet one out from the Earth
e) PERJITU		Rocky planet with the thickest atmosphere
f) SVUEN		Large planet with visible rings
g) SARM		Planet with the smallest orbit

Questions on the Planets

Q3 *The two diagrams below represent photographs taken of a group of stars. The photos were taken a few weeks apart.*

An astronomer noticed that a planet had been captured on both photographs.

a) *Identify the planet* by putting a ring around it.

b) Explain *how* you identified the planet. ....

....

Q4 Use the following words to complete the sentences in the box.

orbit	strong	attraction	stronger	sun	masses

a) Gravity is a force of ________________ that acts between all ____________.

b) When an object is very big, then the gravity will be very ________________.

c) The closer you get to an object, the ______________ its force of gravity will be.

d) The object in the Solar System with the strongest gravity is the ___________.

e) The Moon is held in its __________ by the gravity of the Earth.

Q5 *The picture shows the Earth and the Moon, with a satellite in orbit around the Earth. The satellite is at the same distance from the Earth as it is from the Moon.*

On the picture, draw the direction of the *Earth's* gravitational attraction on the satellite — *label* it E. Also show the direction of the attraction of the *Moon* on the satellite. *Label* it M.

a) Which force of attraction is *greater?* ....

b) Is it *true* or *false* that the satellite is pulling back on the Earth? ....

Questions on the Solar System

Q1 Use the words that follow to fill in the gaps.

Earth	revolved	movement	Sun	change

a) You can tell a planet by its ________________ against the background stars.

b) Sometimes the motion of a planet can ________________ direction in the sky.

c) The first astronomers thought that the ________________ was the centre of the solar system.

d) They thought that everything ________________ around it.

e) However, astronomers after Copernicus realised that the ________________ was what most things revolved around in the solar system.

Q2 *The planet Jupiter has 4 <u>large</u> moons.* Information about them is given in the table:

Name of Moon	Diameter (km)	Time to Orbit Jupiter (Earth days)
Europa	3126	3.5
Callisto	4820	16.7
Io	3632	1.8
Ganymede	5276	7.2

a) Which moon is the *largest?* ....

b) Which moon takes the *longest* time to orbit Jupiter? ....

c) Which moon experiences the *greatest* gravitational acceleration due to Jupiter?

....

Q3 *An astronomer takes a timed photograph of the night sky with a camera that follows the stars.*

When she develops the film, she sees the stars as points, but there are also some *bright lines* across it. She checks, but there were no satellites or planes in the area, and there was no fault on the film.

What *astronomical event* could have caused the lines? ....

Questions on the Solar System

Q4 *In Arizona there is a big crater in the desert. It was not formed by a volcano, but by another natural event.*

a) How was the crater created?

....

....

b) There are *two* reasons why we see *very few* craters like this on the Earth, but see *many thousands* on the Moon. What are the two reasons?

....

....

....

Q5 *Meteors enter the Earth's atmosphere at very high speeds, around 50 miles per second. Most of them get very hot very quickly and burn up.*

a) Name the *force* that causes the meteor to heat up. ....

b) Why do they heat up so quickly? ....

Q6 *The picture below shows the Sun, Earth and Moon.*

a) Draw the shape of the *Moon's orbit* around the Earth.

b) Colour in the half of the Moon that is in *shadow*.

c) Show on the diagram where the Moon is positioned when it appears 'full'. *Label* this position 'F'.

d) In the box on the left, draw a picture of what the Moon would look like from the Earth when it is in the position shown above.

Questions on Satellites

Q1 *Artificial Satellites have been used for different purposes since the first successful launch in 1957. The following statements describe possible motions of satellites.*

A) have high orbits
B) have low orbits
C) move across the sky
D) above the atmosphere
E) orbits in a few hours
F) orbits in 24 hours

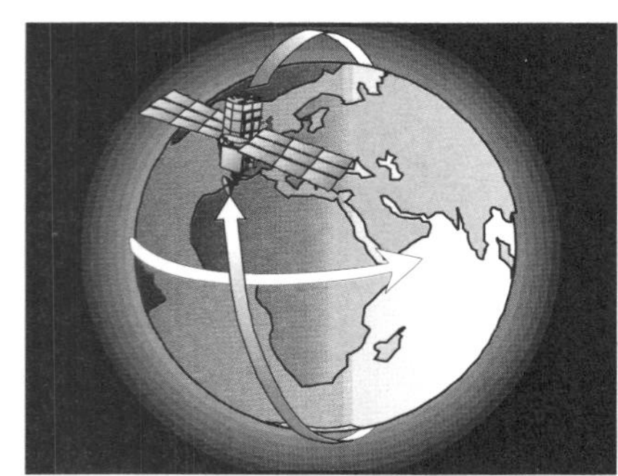

Which of the statements above apply to:

a) most TV satellites? ....

b) spy satellites? ....

Q2 *NASA spent a large amounts of money putting the Hubble Space Telescope into orbit around the Earth.*

a) Why do orbiting telescopes get a *clearer view* of the stars than telescopes located on Earth?

....

....

....

The Space Telescope, like all satellites, needs power for it to work. It uses *solar cells* positioned on 'solar panels'. In the past, satellites often used batteries for power.

b) What is the advantage of using *solar cells* instead of batteries to power satellites?

....

....

c) Why do satellites generally need small rocket motors and fuel sources, even though there is no air resistance in space?

....

....

Questions on Satellites

Q3 *When the Voyager spacecraft were sent off to study Jupiter, Saturn, Uranus and Neptune, they had* *__nuclear generators__* *on board rather than solar cell arrays.*

a) Why could not solar cells have been used? ....

....

b) Why do you think some people were concerned when Voyager was launched?

....

Q4 *Satellite facts. For each statement, decide whether it is* *__true__* *or* *__false__*, *and put a tick in the corresponding box.*

True	False	
☐	☐	**a)** The first artificial satellite was launched in 1957.
☐	☐	**b)** Satellites must burn fuel all the time to stay in orbit.
☐	☐	**c)** Satellites are useful for seeing what the weather is doing.
☐	☐	**d)** The Moon can be regarded as a natural satellite of the Earth.
☐	☐	**e)** Orbiting satellites are always accelerating.
☐	☐	**f)** Some satellites orbit in the Earth's atmosphere.
☐	☐	**g)** Satellites send information by radio waves.

Q5 *This picture shows the Earth with two identical artificial satellites in circular orbits around it. Satellite 2 is further away from Earth than Satellite 1.*

Satellite 1

Satellite 2

a) Which satellite will require the *__greatest__* amount of energy to put it into orbit?

....

b) Which satellite will orbit in the *__shortest__* time?

....

c) Although satellites and other bits of 'space junk' sometimes fall back towards Earth, usually very little reaches the Earth's surface. Why is this?

....

d) Designers of satellites spend very little time and effort making them streamlined. Why?

....

....

Questions on Days and Seasons

Q1 Draw arrows to match the descriptions around the outside with the boxes in the middle:

The time taken for the Earth to rotate once.

Locations along this always have 12 hours of day and 12 hours of night.

What people on the side of the Earth facing the Sun are experiencing.

On June 21st, someone here will have 24 hours of daylight.

What one hemisphere of the Earth is doing when it is winter.

What the average temperature should do during summer.

What causes seasons on the Earth and other planets.

The equinox season when the days are getting shorter, and the nights are getting longer.

Above the South Pole, the Sun never does this on December 21st.

The time taken for one full orbit of the Sun by the Earth.

The season that the southern hemisphere is experiencing when the northern hemisphere is experiencing spring.

The direction where the Sun appears to rise for us in the U.K.

24 HOURS

NORTH POLE

AUTUMN

EQUATOR

DAYTIME

SET

TILT OF AXIS

365 DAYS

RISE

TILTING AWAY FROM THE SUN

EAST

AUTUMN

Q2 *A planet in a mythical solar system takes 12 Earth years to revolve around its star, and it spins on its axis once every 30 Earth hours.*

a) How long in Earth time does a *day* last on this planet? ....

c) If the planet's axis is tilted, how long does each *season* last? ....

d) If the planet's axis is *not tilted*, will it experience seasonal changes? ....

e) If the planet's star is *identical* to the Sun, will it appear *bigger* or *smaller* when seen from the planet, than the Sun does when seen from Earth? ....

Questions on Days and Seasons

Q3 *The picture below shows the Earth in its orbit.* Study it and then answer the following questions:

a) What season is it in the *Northern Hemisphere?* ....

b) Write the letter corresponding to a place where the Sun is *just setting*. ....

c) Write the letter corresponding to a place where it will be *dark* for 24 hours. ....

d) If there are no clouds, what will be seen at P? ....

e) If there are no clouds, what will be seen at Q? ....

f) Write the letter corresponding to the position of the *North Pole*. ....

Q4 Check out the wordsearch and ring the answers to the following clues:

a) The season with the longest days.
b) What the Earth's axis has.
c) North and south, where a compass points.
d) The season in which plants start to grow faster.
e) Cold season.
f) The tilt of this causes seasons.
g) 24 hours make a...
h) The nights are this in winter.
i) 365 days make a...
j) How much of the Earth is a hemisphere?

S	U	M	M	E	R	F	Y	I	T
G	W	X	Z	S	Y	C	D	L	I
E	L	O	P	A	I	N	F	V	L
B	N	O	R	W	D	X	L	C	T
S	P	R	I	N	G	Y	A	D	Q
I	A	F	L	N	C	Z	H	U	N
M	A	D	O	T	F	R	A	E	Y
X	F	L	W	I	N	T	E	R	I

Q5 *The Earth moves around the Sun in an elliptical (oval) shaped orbit. It is closest to the Sun in January when the distance between the two is 91.5 million miles, and is furthest from the Sun in July, when the distance between the two is 94.5 million miles.*

Explain why the average winter temperature in the northern hemisphere is *higher* than that in the southern hemisphere.

....

....

....

Questions on the Universe

Q1 *All the objects that we see around us in the Universe started off as clouds of gas and dust.*

a) What caused the clouds to collapse?

....

b) What *two* types of energy are produced inside a such a cloud when the nuclear reactions start? ....

Q2 *The Solar System is part of the Milky Way.*

a) What is the *Milky Way?* ....

b) What sort of shape does it have?

....

c) How many stars are there in the Milky Way? Choose the closest answer:

☐ **HUNDREDS** ☐ **THOUSANDS** ☐ **MILLIONS** ☐ **BILLIONS**

Q3 Below are some statements about the Milky Way. Decide if each is *true* or *false*, and tick the relevant box.

True	False	
☐	☐	**a)** The Milky Way is about 10,000 light years across.
☐	☐	**b)** The Milky Way is at the centre of the Universe.
☐	☐	**c)** Our Solar System is at the centre of the Milky Way.
☐	☐	**d)** The Milky Way has spiral arms.
☐	☐	**e)** All the stars that we see at night are part of the Milky Way.
☐	☐	**f)** The Milky Way takes a very long time to rotate.
☐	☐	**g)** The Milky Way is the biggest galaxy of its kind.
☐	☐	**h)** The Milky Way is separated from its neighbours by lots of space.
☐	☐	**i)** There are still gas clouds in the Milky Way.
☐	☐	**j)** No more stars will form in the Milky Way.
☐	☐	**k)** The Milky Way is held together by the force of gravity.
☐	☐	**l)** Neighbouring stars in the Milky Way are usually much further apart than the planets in the Solar System.

Questions on the Universe

Q4 Look at the table below, then answer the questions that follow it.

Distance from	Distance
Earth to Sun	8 light minutes
Earth to nearest star from Sun	4.2 light years
Earth to star in question	10 light years

a) If something happened on the Sun, *how long* would it take before people on the Earth found out about it? ....

b) If the star nearest to the Sun exploded, *how long* would it be before we knew about it?

....

c) If the inhabitants of a planet orbiting this star had a big laser, and shone it in our direction, how long would it take for the *reflection* to get back to them? ....

Q5 List these objects in their usual *order of size*, smallest first:

galaxy moon meteorite star universe planet solar system

Order:

....

Q6 Solve the clues and put the answers into the crossword:

Across

2. What a light year is a measure of. (7)
4. The fastest thing in the Universe. (5)
6. The largest object in our Solar System. (3)
7. Stars form from clouds of dust and... (3)
8. The length of time it takes light to travel one light year in distance. (4)

Down

1. How many stars there are in our Milky Way galaxy. (8)
3. An example of a rocky planet. (5)
5. The force that holds the Milky Way together. (7)
6. Our Sun is an example. (4)

Q7 *'The Sky at Night' TV broadcasts have been going on for over forty years now, and have been beamed (by accident) into space for this length of time. An advanced civilisation living 30 light years away has been looking out for signs of aliens like us.*
For what length of time might Patrick Moore have been a possible TV star *to them?*

....

Questions on The Life Cycle of Stars

Q1 *Astronomers looking around in our galaxy can see lots of gas and dust. They also see stars, and have come up with some ideas about how the stars have been formed from the gas and dust.* Use these words to *complete the passages* below:

potential dust light large nuclear gravitational rises energy gas high heat planet many collapse doesn't star heat

The raw material for making stars is found in clouds of ______________ and ______________. Like everything else having mass, ______________ forces exist within the clouds. This pulls the particles together, causing the clouds to ______________ inwards towards the centre. As they do this, gravitational ______________ ______________ is converted into ______________ energy. When this happens the temperature ______________.

If the mass in the middle is ______________ enough, the temperature may get so ______________ that ______________ reactions begin. When this happens, massive amounts of ______________ energy and ______________ energy are given out, thus creating a new ______________.

If there is not enough mass, then it ______________ gets hot enough, and instead of a star forming, a ______________ is formed. This is why we get stars and planets forming together, and why astronomers think that there are ______________ solar systems in our galaxy.

Q2 *The three descriptions below describe three stages of star formation.* Match the *labels* above them to the *correct description* by drawing an arrow from each:

PROTOSTAR

Particles are very hot and tightly packed. They move very fast and collide. Collisions are so hard that nuclear reactions occur.

CLOUD OF GAS AND DUST

Particles widely spaced and moving slowly. There is a lot of gravitational potential energy. Collisions very rare and release no nuclear energy.

NEW STAR

Particles are gaining energy and moving faster. Collisions take place more often, but are not hard enough to release nuclear energy.

An Outer Space A-Z

Are you saturn comfortably? Well, see if you can solve this Outer Space A to Z. Answer the clues in the boxes. The numbers after the clue give the number of letters for the answer.

A) the name for the science of studying outer space. ______________. (9)

B) a big one started off the Universe. ______________. (4)

C) name for a group of fixed stars. ______________. (13)

D) length of time for a planet to spin on its axis. ______________. (3)

E) third planet from the Sun. ______________. (5)

F) gravity is an example of this. ______________. (5)

G) collection of millions of stars and solar systems. ______________. (6)

H) the name for half of a planet. ______________. (10)

I) the Sun does this to the Earth. ______________. (11)

J) largest planet in our Solar System. ______________. (7)

K) last letter of the colour of space. ______________. (5)

L) the fastest thing in the Universe. ______________. (5)

M) fourth planet in our Solar System. ______________. (4)

N) what a cloud of gas and dust is sometimes called. ______________. (6)

O) the name for the path of a planet around a star. ______________. (5)

P) a cool object that orbits around a star. ______________. (6)

Q) because sound can't travel through a vacuum, space is ______________. (5)

R) what planets do to the Sun's light so we can see it. ______________. (7)

S) a huge ball of gas that gives off heat and light. ______________. (4)

T) what scientists use to look out into space. ______________. (9)

U) the name for all the space and matter we know about. ______________. (8)

V) what space is because there's no air. ______________. (6)

W) a liquid, recently found frozen on the Moon! ______________. (5)

X) a type of radiation that all stars give out. ______________. (4)

Y) the length of time for a planet to orbit a star. ______________. (4)

Z) the number of people living on the moon right now. ______________. (4)

Outer Space Activity Page

Q1 Use the clues to fill in the crossword. All the answers are things to do with space.

Across

4. Name of the track followed by a planet. (5)
6. Earth does this about its axis. (6)
9. Instrument scientists use to look far into space. (9)
11. The waves used to contact satellites. (5)
12. Force attracting satellites to Earth. (6)

Down

1. Vehicle needed to take a satellite above the atmosphere. (6)
2. There is none of this in space to cause friction. (3)
3. Our Milky Way is an example of this. (6,6)
5. This is a natural satellite of the Earth. (4)
7. This changes with the seasons and becomes more pleasant during summer. (7)
8. We sometimes see satellites because they do this to the Sun's light. (7)
10. Solar cells convert solar energy into this. (11)

Q2 *The table below shows information about four planets.*
Look at the information in the table, then answer the questions that follow it.

Planet	Distance from Sun (millions of km)	Time to spin on Axis (hours)	Time to complete Orbit (years)
Earth	150	24	1
P	230	25	1.9
Q	778	10	12
R	108	5856	0.6

a) Which planet is *closest* to the Sun? ....

b) Which planet has the *shortest day?* ....

c) Which planet is represented by the letter P? ....

d) From which planet would you expect the Sun to look *dimmest?* ....

e) How does the time taken to complete *one orbit* change as the distance from the star *increases?* ....

....

f) Which planet, when seen from Earth, will show *phases* like the Moon? ....

Pictorial Outer Space Wordsearch

The clues to this wordsearch are in the pictures below. All you have to do is find the missing words in each of the sentences and work out the names of the things the arrows are pointing to. In each case the number of letters is given by the number in the rings.

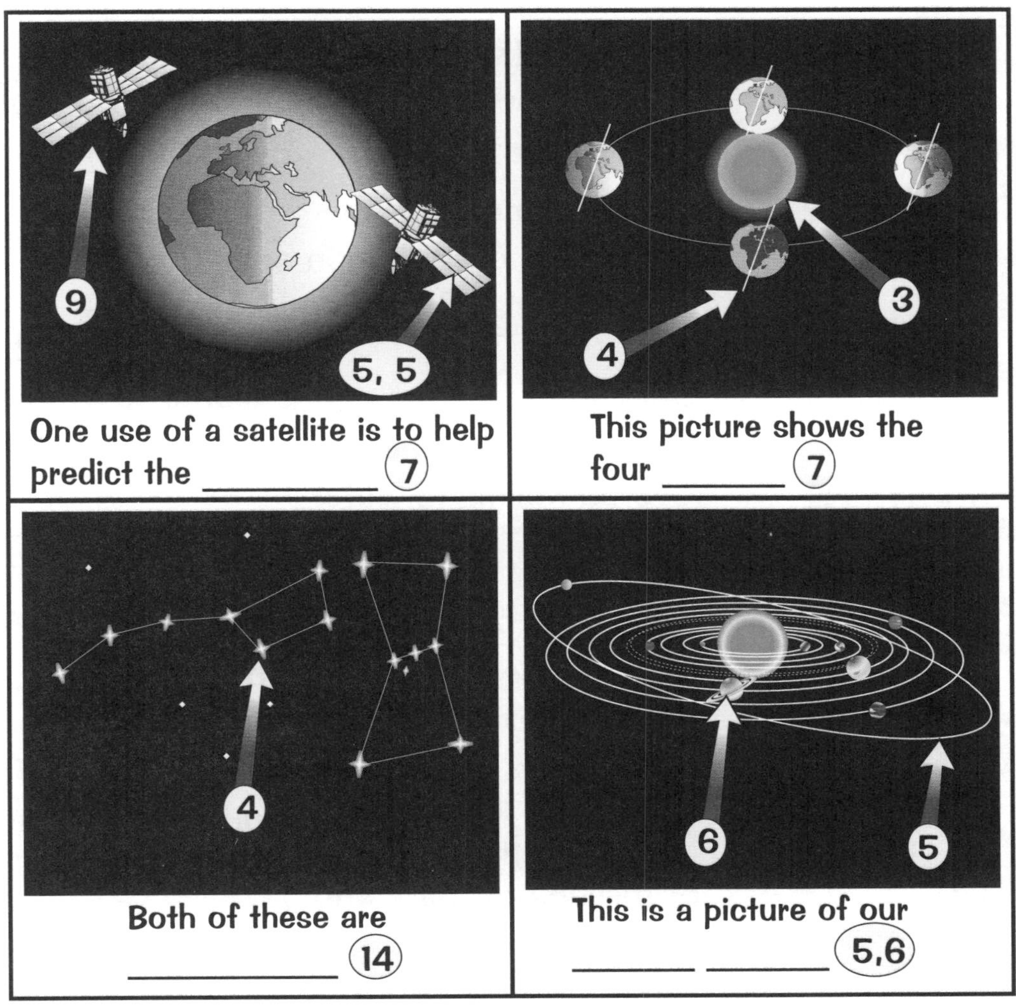

S	H	J	B	J	U	H	B	S	A	T	U	R	N	H
O	R	B	I	T	E	J	A	E	J	H	F	U	G	F
L	G	W	D	T	S	U	N	A	G	A	D	E	J	D
A	J	G	E	G	D	H	H	D	H	H	X	D	U	S
R	U	F	F	A	G	S	A	T	E	L	L	I	T	E
P	E	D	D	D	T	G	G	T	S	H	U	F	S	A
A	D	H	J	J	G	H	J	G	T	Q	E	D	E	S
N	J	X	U	W	F	U	E	F	A	V	D	U	D	O
E	G	G	E	E	D	E	J	R	R	H	J	E	J	N
L	C	O	N	S	T	E	L	L	A	T	I	O	N	S

Outer Space Revision

Q1 In this solar system there are a number of objects and some definitions. Draw curves connecting the *objects* with their *definitions*.

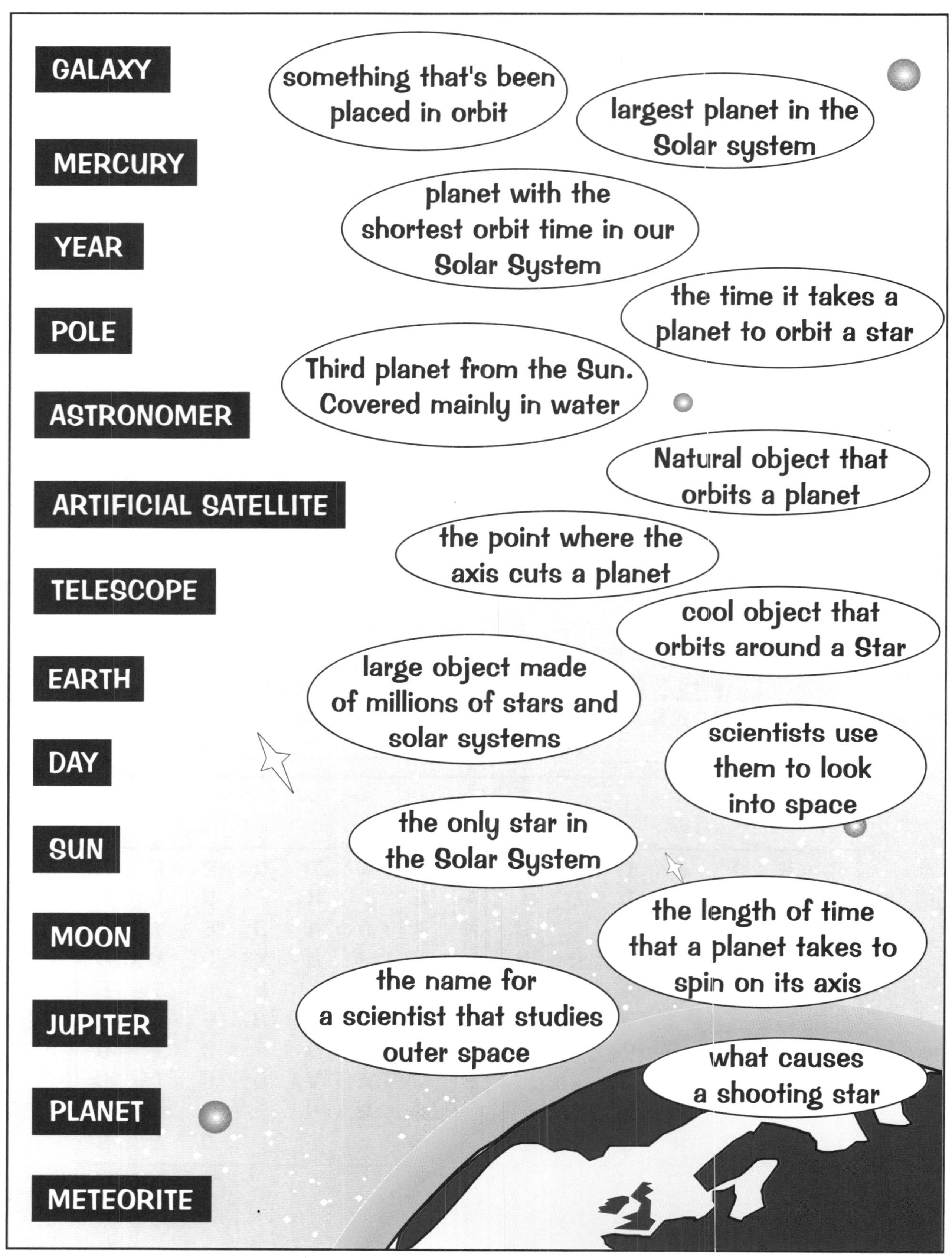

General Questions on Space

Q1 *The Moon orbits the Earth once every 28 days. It also rotates about its axis during this time but always manages to keep the same face pointing towards us.*

a) How many Earth days does it take for the Moon to rotate *once* on its axis? ....

b) How many Earth days does *daylight* last for on the Moon's equator? ....

Q2 *Mars has polar ice caps which change size, getting bigger and smaller alternatively, as Mars orbits around the Sun.* Explain why the ice caps change size in this way. (Hint: consider why the ice might solidify and melt as Mars goes around the Sun).

....

....

....

Q3 *The Russian space station, Mir, once suffered a collision with a cargo carrier, which damaged some of its solar panels and caused the space station to start rotating. This caused a drop in Mir's power supply.* Give *two reasons* why the level of power dropped?

....

....

Q4 *Because of all the dust and gas that surrounds newly formed stars, astronomers can't see them directly. Fortunately, all warm objects emit infra-red light, and because the dust surrounding new stars is warm, astronomers can see them using infra-red detecting telescopes. Unfortunately, the Earth's atmosphere absorbs most infra-red light coming from space!*

a) Where should astronomers place their telescopes if they want to see newly formed stars?

....

b) Infra-red detecting telescopes are kept at very very low temperatures. Why is this?

....

....

Q5 *Stars in galaxies all move around at very high speeds (typically 200*km/s). Why is it that galaxies don't fly apart?

....

....

Questions on Types of Energy

Q1 *This first question is all about energy types, to see if you recognise the 10 types. To make it easier, we've split it into two halves.* Look at the thing with energy, and *tick* the column of the energy type that you think there's *most of*.

a)

Thing with energy	Electrical	Light	Sound	Kinetic	Nuclear
i) Atom bomb					
ii) Wire carrying a 'phone conversation					
iii) A speeding bullet					
iv) A crying baby					
v) A piece of glowing magnesium					

b)

Thing with energy	Thermal (Heat)	Radiant (Infra Red)	Gravitational Potential	Elastic Potential	Chemical
i) A squashed Jack in the Box					
ii) A plate balancing on a pole					
iii) A high calorie birthday cake					
iv) A red hot, glowing rivet					
v) A hot water bottle					

Q2 Match each of the nine examples of things with energy to the main type of energy they have, by writing them in the correct part of the table below. One of them has been done for you.

Type of Energy	Example
Chemical	____________
	____________
	____________
Light	tv screen
	____________
	____________
Kinetic	____________
	____________
	____________

petrol
desk lamp
battery
rollercoaster
tv screen
coal
L.E.D.
wind
tennis ball

Questions on Energy Transfer

Q3 *Energy is only important when it is changed from one type into another.* Here all you have to do is to match up the *Examples* with the *Energy Changes*. The first one is done for you.

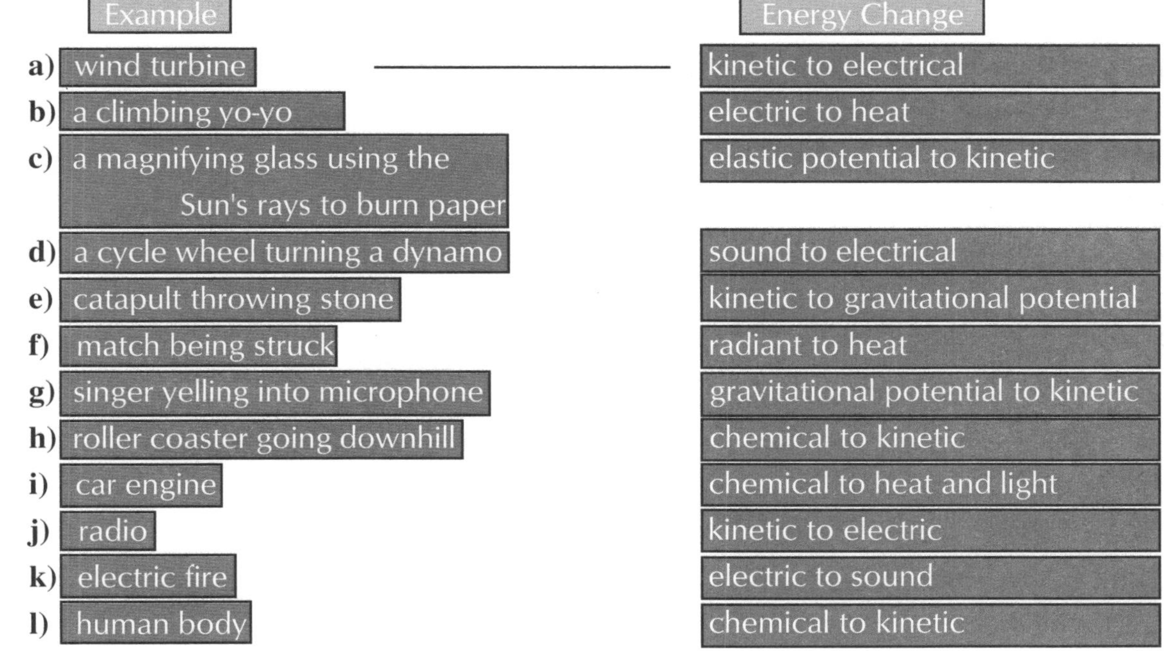

	Example	Energy Change
a)	wind turbine	kinetic to electrical
b)	a climbing yo-yo	electric to heat
c)	a magnifying glass using the Sun's rays to burn paper	elastic potential to kinetic
d)	a cycle wheel turning a dynamo	sound to electrical
e)	catapult throwing stone	kinetic to gravitational potential
f)	match being struck	radiant to heat
g)	singer yelling into microphone	gravitational potential to kinetic
h)	roller coaster going downhill	chemical to kinetic
i)	car engine	chemical to heat and light
j)	radio	kinetic to electric
k)	electric fire	electric to sound
l)	human body	chemical to kinetic

Q4 Fill in the diagram below to show the energy changes involved when coal is burned.

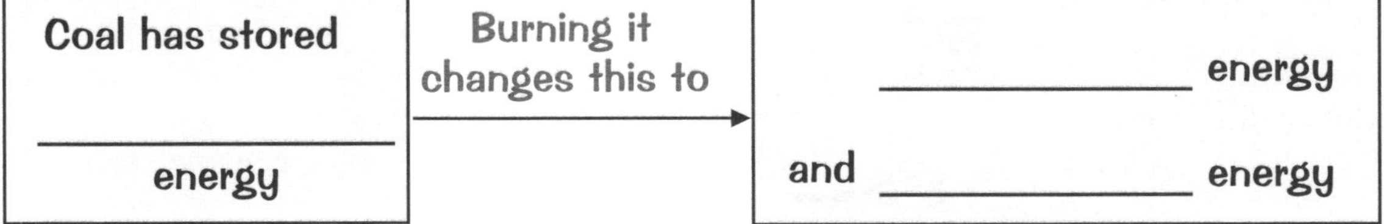

Q5 Below is a diagram of a man firing an arrow into a target. Fill in the boxes by deciding what type of energy changes occurs at each of the three stages.

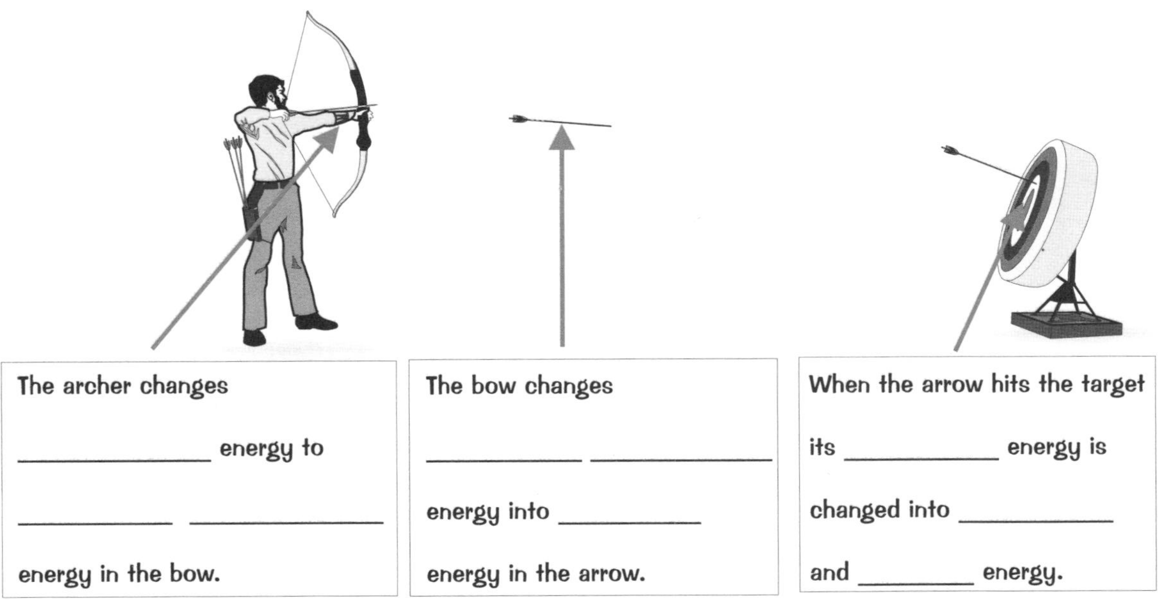

Questions on Conservation of Energy

Q1 *Complete* the following sentences which summarise the Principle of the Conservation of Energy:

Energy can never be .... or ....

It is only ever .... from one form to another.

Q2 *Look at the energy flow diagram shown here.* For each of the examples given below, draw an energy flow diagram. The first one has been done for you.

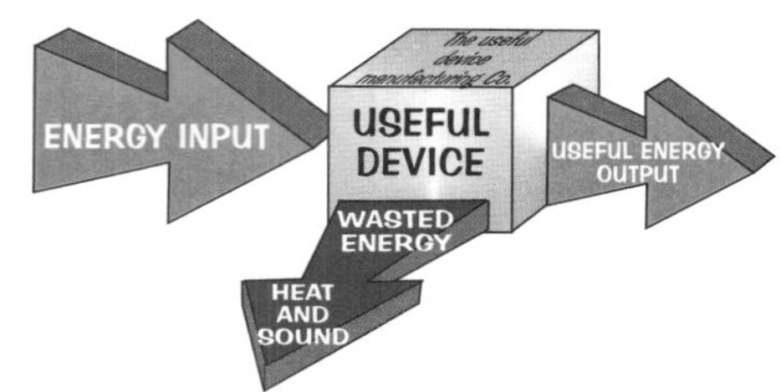

a) electric hoist.

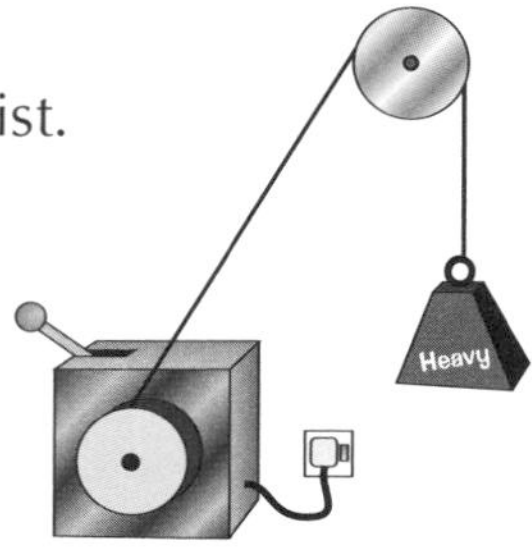

Electric energy → HOIST → potential energy of load
↓
wasted sound and heat

b) electric light bulb.

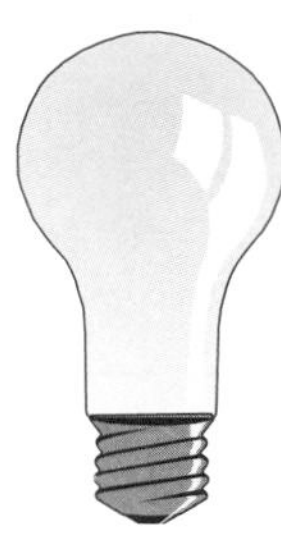

c) petrol-driven car.

d) weightlifter lifting a weight.

e) computer monitor.

Questions on Conservation of Energy

Q3 *Charlie has been doing some experiments with an electric motor. The motor takes in electrical energy and then does some work. Charlie has measured the amount of energy input into the motor, and then the work that it has done.*
The results are shown in the table. Look at the table and then answer the questions.

Time the motor is switched on for (secs)	Energy Input (?)	Useful work done by motor (?)	
10	5	2	
20	10	6	
30	15	10	
40	20	17	
50	25	24	

a) What will be the units of energy input? ....

b) What are the units for useful work done? ....

c) Add a column headed **Energy Wasted** to the table, and work out the answers.

d) *Charlie looks at his results and makes a prediction. "When the motor is switched on for 60 seconds, the energy input will be 30."* What do you think?

....

e) He predicts that the useful work done will be 32 energy units. Do you agree? ....

Q4 Use the following words to complete these sentences.

sound	efficiency	output	machine	input	heat	wasted

We call something that changes one type of energy into another a ________________. We call the energy supplied to the machine the Total Energy ________________. The useful work that the machine does is called the Useful Energy ________________. Looking at these two numbers tells us how much energy is ________________, usually as ________________ energy or ________________ energy. We can also get the ________________.

Q5 *Energy Anagrams.*
Look at the clues and the letters, and work out the answers.

	Letters	Clue	Answer
a)	CIKNIET	Type of energy that moving objects have	
b)	SCOERNDEV	Energy is never created nor destroyed. It is ...	
c)	ATHE	Energy is wasted as sound or	
d)	HEAMCIN	What we call something that changes energy from one type to another	
e)	LIMCHECA	Cars use a lot of this type of energy	
f)	FLUESU	The energy that we want produced is	

Questions on Energy Efficiency

Q1 *This is a crossword about* *Energy Efficiency*

Look at the clues and fill in the answers to the crossword in the blanks.

Across:

2. Energy is wasted as this type (5 letters)
5. This is the partner type of energy to 2 across (4 letters)
6. If it's out of a hundred, efficiency is in this (7 letters)
7. The energy that comes in is called this (5 letters)
9. This tells us how good a machine is (10 letters)

Down:

1. The efficiency can be between zero and ....(3 letters)
3. This is the energy that the machine delivers (6 letters)
4. One of these changes energy from one type to another (7 letters)
8. What you do with the output and input to get the efficiency (6 letters)
10. The lowest efficiency that a machine could have (6 letters)

Q2 *Sandra and Sheryl are carrying out an experiment to measure the efficiency of an electric motor.*

A joulemeter measures the energy going into the motor. They drag a force over a measured distance to get the output energy.

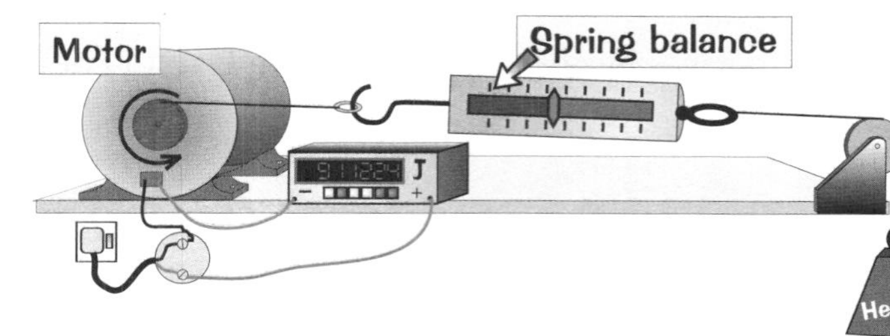

Help them by *completing* their results table.

Energy Input ( )	Pulling Force ( )	Distance Moved ( )	Energy Output ( )	Efficiency ( )
10	4	2		
10	3	3		
20	6		18	
20	5			0.75
5	4	1		

Questions on Energy Efficiency

Q3 *This is a picture which shows the different sorts of energy involved in making a car go.*

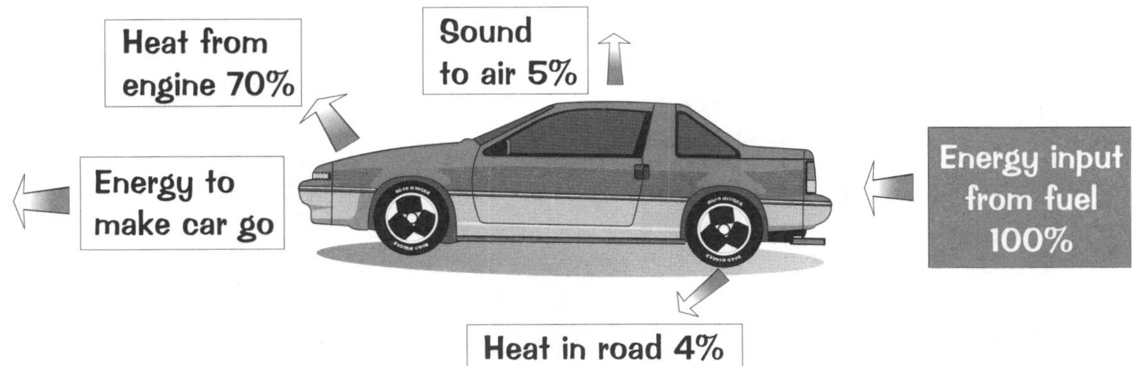

a) Work out the *percentage* of energy that actually makes the car go.

....

b) What name do scientists give to *movement energy?* ....

c) What is the name of the *force* that *slows* all moving objects down? ....

d) In what part of a car do we want to be able to change lots of *movement* energy to *heat* when needed? ....

Q4 *A lot of power stations in Britain burn coal for energy. A flow chart can be used to show how energy from the coal gets to be electricity.*

Coal burned to heat water → Water changes to steam → Steam used to turn turbines → Turbines turn generators → Generators make electricity

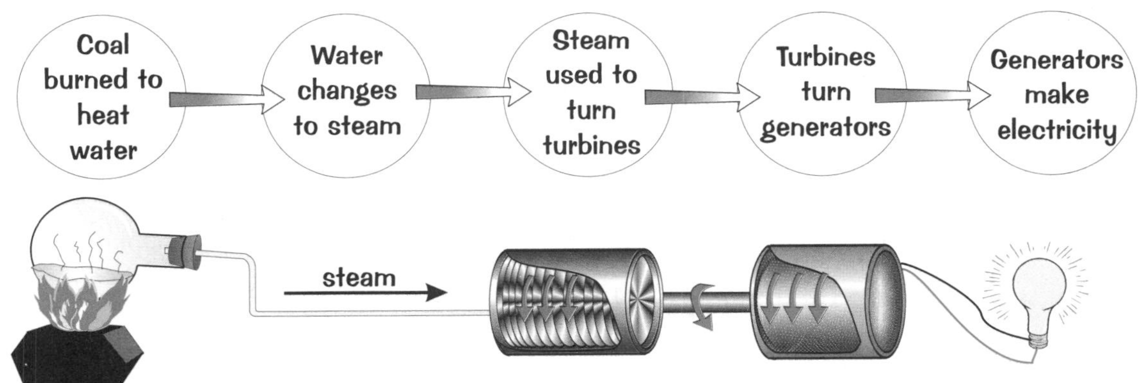

For each of the following statements, *tick the box* to indicate whether they are *True* or *False*.

Statement	True	False
a) The coal contains chemical energy		
b) The amount of electrical energy produced is the same as the enegy in the coal		
c) Energy is lost as heat ans sound energy		
d) The energy in the coal came from the Earth		
e) Coal is a non-renewable energy resource		

Questions on Work Done, Energy and Power

Q1 *Derek has a set of dominoes. He and Sharon have played a game. You can see the pieces laid out here.*

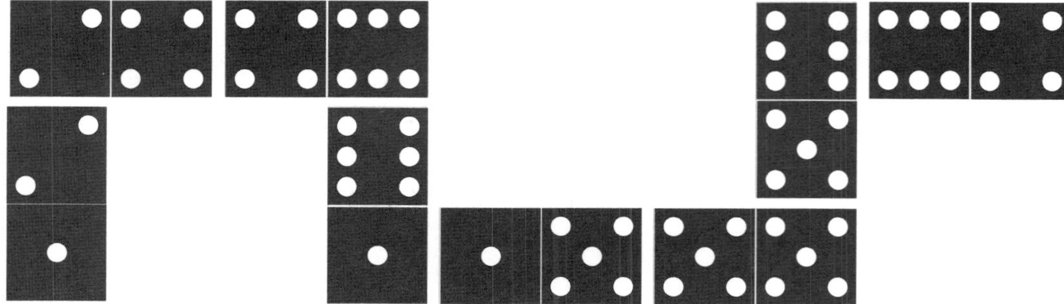

The two of them notice something very interesting. They have been answering work, energy and power questions. All the answers to the questions appear as dominoes.

e.g. if the answer was 23, then it would match with domino.

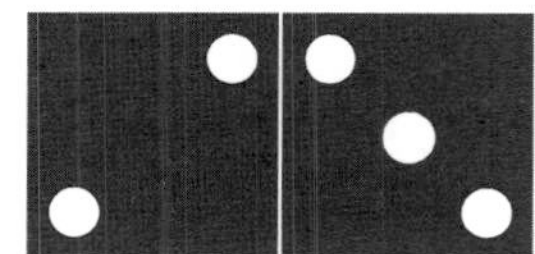

Only one domino is not covered by a question.
All you have to do is to work out the answer to each of the sums, tick off the dominoes and work out which is the odd domino out.
These equations will help you.

Energy (joules) = Force Moved (newtons) x Distance moved (metres)

Powers (watts) = Energy Used (joules) / Time taken (seconds)

a) How much *work* is done when 5 newtons moves through 3 metres? ....

b) A force of 7 N moves through 8 m, how much *energy* is used? ....

c) 2 newtons and 12 metres. How much *work* is done? ....

d) 64 J of work is done. The force is 1 N. *How far* has it moved? ....

e) 96 J of energy is used up in 8 s, what is the *power* in watts? ....

f) An electric motor has a power of 5 watts. How much *energy* does it use in 11 seconds?

....

g) A stereo has a power of 10 watts. *How long* before it uses up 610 joules of energy?

....

h) Which domino is the *odd one out?* ....

Questions on Work Done, Energy and Power

Q2 *This question is all about units.* You have to solve the anagrams, and then match up the unit with whatever it measures. The units measure *Force, Distance moved, Energy, Time and Power.*

Anagram	Solution	Symbol	Used to measure
TENNOW	....	....	....
REETM	....	....	....
OLEUJ	....	....	....
SCODNE	....	....	....
TATW	....	....	....

Q3 Are the following statements *true* or *false?*

a) Power is the same as force. ....

b) Power is not the same as energy. ....

c) Energy is measured in joules. ....

d) One watt is a joule per second. ....

e) A more powerful machine will do a job quicker than a less powerful one. ....

Q4 *Karl is fitting an electric motor to his radio-controlled car. It's a 50 watt motor. It can move the car along a straight track in 5 seconds. The car has mass 0.5kg.*

a) How much *energy* does the motor use in the 5 seconds?

....

b) The car crosses the finish line at 7m/s. How much *kinetic energy* has it got? Kinetic energy = $^1/_2$ mV^2

....

c) Explain the *difference* between your answers to parts (a) and (b).

....

....

Questions on Temperature

Q1 Look at these pictures of 3 molecules from different pieces of the same material. *They are vibrating differently because they are at different temperatures.* Colour them in differently, and label them as **Hot**, **Warm** and **Cold**. Include a key to your colouring

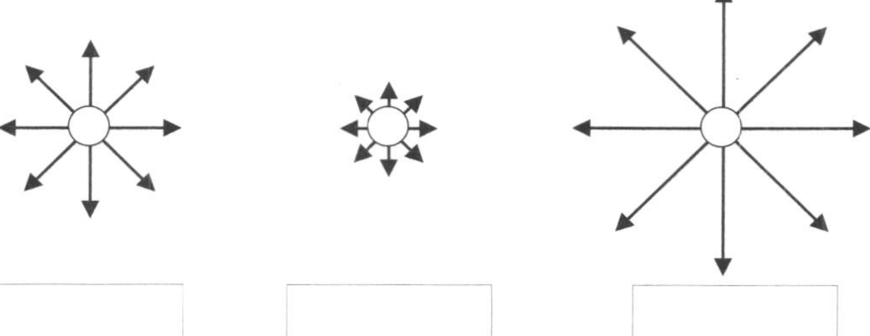

Colour for Hot	
Colour for Warm	
Colour for Cold	

Q2 In this question, you have to match up the *Object* with the *Temperature* (in degrees Celsius) in the right hand column.

Object	Temperature (°C)
Normal Human Body	0
Boiling Point of Pure water	6000
Coldest weather temperature	37
Outside of the Sun	100
Absolute Zero	-50
Freezing Point of pure water	-273

Q3 *Comparing Temperatures. In this question, there are some pairs of descriptions.* All you have to do is to put a *ring* around the example that has the *higher* temperature.

a) boiling water / melting ice.

b) hot coffee / human body.

c) melting mercury / hot summer's day.

d) human body / hot bath.

e) melting iron / boiling water.

f) melting ice / melting mercury.

Q4 *The thermometers that school pupils once used contained mercury.*

a) Why was a different liquid found? ....

b) What sort of liquid is used now? ....

Questions on Temperature

Q5 *In this question, there are a number of different substances.* Draw arrows to show which way *heat energy* will flow between them.

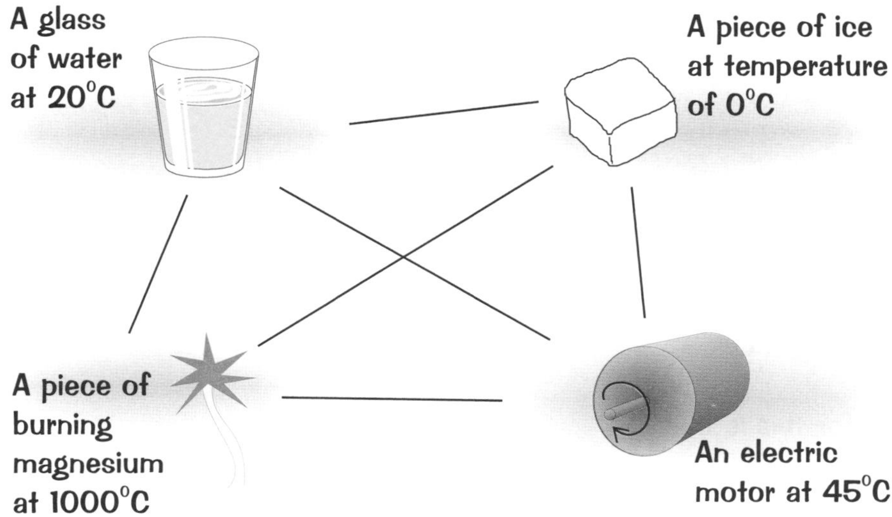

Q6 In each of the following, you have to choose the correct option for the sentence to make sense. Put a *ring* around the correct word(s).

a) We use a **(joulemeter / thermometer)** to measure temperature.
b) A hotter molecule will be vibrating **(more / less)** than a colder one.
c) Heat energy will always flow from a hot object to a **(hotter / colder)** one.
d) Temperature is measured in **(seconds / degrees)**.
e) Heat is a form of **(energy / power)** and it is measured in **(degrees / joules)**.
f) On the Celsius scale, the freezing point of water is **(0 / 32)** degrees.
g) On the Celsius scale, the boiling point of water is **(100 / 212)** degrees.
h) Particles stop vibrating at **(the freezing point / absolute zero)**.
i) Absolute zero is **(0 / -273)** degrees Celsius.

Q7 *A standard laboratory thermometer contains a number of features to enable it to be used to measure temperatures accurately.* Match up the *Feature* with the *Reason for the design*.

	Feature	Reason for the design
a)	Large bulb and long narrow scale	Liquids expand regularly with temperature
b)	Vacuum above liquid	Thermometer reacts quickly
c)	Bulb is made of thin glass	The thermometer is sensitive
d)	Temperature scale is regular	The liquid expands easily

Questions on Expansion

Q1 *The picture below shows a flask full of air, with a long tube in. The tube is being held under the water in a beaker.*

One person from the class puts their sweaty hands round the flask.

Choose the correct answer from each of the following and put a *tick* next to it.

a) Would you see

i) water going up the tube?

ii) air bubbles coming out of the tube?

iii) the flask explode?

b) The reason for this is that

i) heat goes from their hands to the air making it contract.

ii) heat goes from their hands to the air making it expand.

iii) only the glass of the flask expands.

iv) air from the flask dissolves in the water.

c) Substances expand when they are heated. The reason for this is that

i) the molecules vibrate more so that they take up more space?

ii) the molecules themselves get bigger when they get hotter?

iii) gas molecules from the air enter the structure of the substance?

Q2 *Sasha's science class are shown an experiment. A metal ball on a chain will just fit through a metal ring on a wooden handle.*
Put a *ring* around the correct word(s).

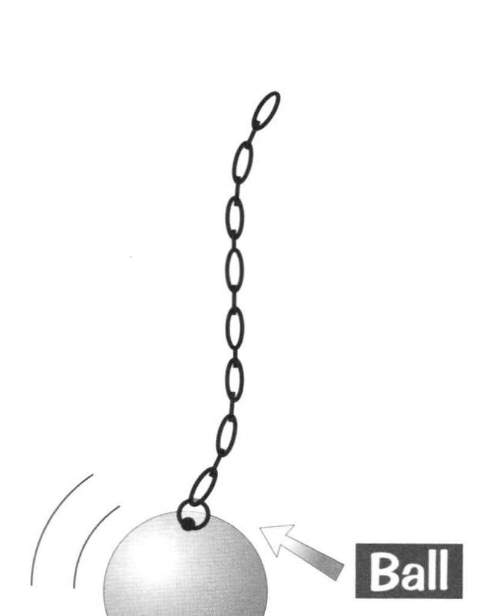

a) When the ball is heated strongly over a bunsen burner, then it **(will still/ will not)** go through the metal ring.

b) This is because the ball has got **(bigger/smaller)** as it is heated.

c) It does this because the molecules have got **(bigger/ further apart)**.

d) A way of getting the ball through the ring again would be to **(heat/ cool)** the ring.

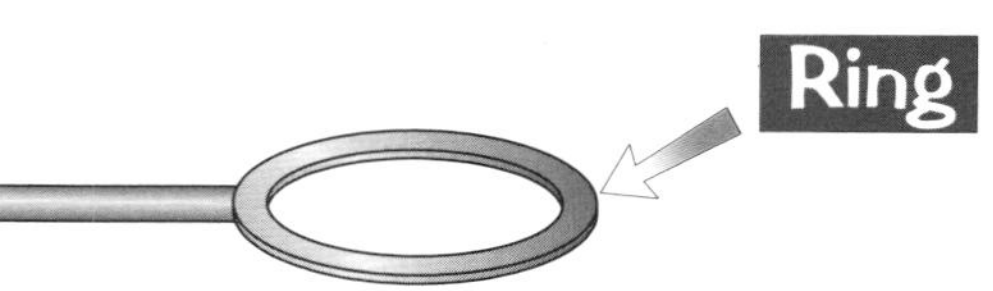

e) When they have both been allowed to cool down, the ball will **(fit through again/ still not fit through)**.

Questions on Expansion

Q3

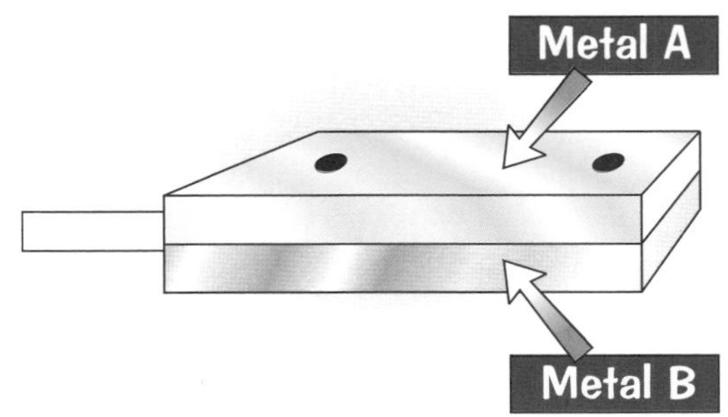

A bimetallic strip is a device that's made from two types of metal, pinned together as in the picture here.

For a particular temperature rise, Metal A expands more then Metal B. The only way that the bimetallic strip can allow this is for it to bend.

In the following questions, say whether the *bimetallic strip* has been *heated* or *cooled*. Indicate the correct answer by *circling* it.

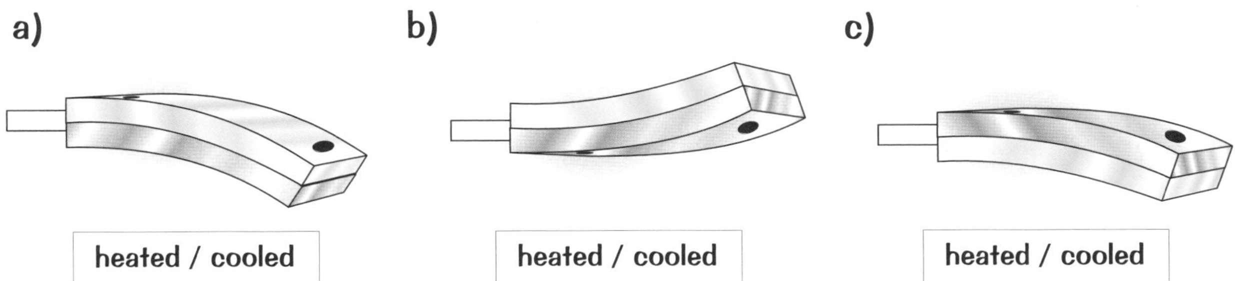

Q4 Find the answers to the clues in the Wordsearch.

a) Temperature is measured in degrees ....?.............
b) What substances do when they are heated.
c) When heated the molecules get further ....?..........
d) This is the temperature of pure melting ice.
e) Molecules do NOT get smaller or ......?....... when they are heated.
f) This is used to measure temperature.
g) These particles vibrate more than cold ones.
h) If the temperature goes down, it can get .....?......
i) What we call the "hotness" of something.
j) There are a hundred of these between melting ice and boiling steam.

A	C	F	N	G	L	P	R	Z	N	G
T	E	M	P	E	R	A	T	U	R	E
O	L	R	E	T	T	O	H	L	P	X
M	S	D	H	S	L	V	E	G	Q	P
R	I	M	N	T	U	T	R	A	P	A
H	U	A	P	A	R	T	M	A	Z	N
Y	S	F	R	N	D	L	O	C	H	D
H	Z	Y	Q	Z	N	T	M	N	F	L
G	D	C	D	E	G	R	E	E	S	X
R	N	Q	L	R	F	R	T	T	N	S
H	D	S	T	O	U	W	E	X	L	F
D	S	B	I	G	G	E	R	R	T	N

Q5 When they are assembled, some parts of a jet engine, such as the turbine blades, do not fit well. They are too loose and rattle about. Explain why this is alright once the engine is going.

....

....

Questions on Heat Transfer

Q1 *In this question, there are a number of statements about Heat Transfer.* Decide whether they are concerned with *Conduction*, *Convection*, *Radiation* or *All Three* and tick the appropriate column(s) of the table.

	Conduction	Convection	Radiation
A Heat flows between two places when there is a difference in temperature.			
B Where heat is passed from molecule to molecule; most effective in solid metals.			
C Occurs through transparent substances.			
D Sets up movement currents in liquids and gases.			
E It is affected by colour and shininess.			
F Hotter particles move around faster than slower ones.			
G This can occur through a vacuum.			
H This is caused by hot fluid expanding and rising.			

Q2 The paragraph that follows is all about heat conduction. You have to use the words in the coloured box to fill in the gaps. The words may be used ONCE, MORE THAN ONCE or NOT AT ALL.

neighbouring collide carry reflect electrons pockets
vibrate close good poor solids

Conduction of heat occurs mainly in .... This is because the particles are relatively .... Extra heat energy makes the particles .... more. They pass on the extra vibration energy to .... particles. It works well in solids because the particles are .... to each other. Metals are .... conductors of heat energy because they contain many free .... which can move through the solid and .... the energy. The electrons give up their energy when they .... with other particles.

Questions on Heat Transfer

Q3 Write down three *insulating* substances and three *conducting* substances in the table below and then complete the other columns.

Name of Substance	Conductor or Insulator	Used for

Q4 *The diagram shows a beach and some land by the seaside. It is a hot sunny day.*

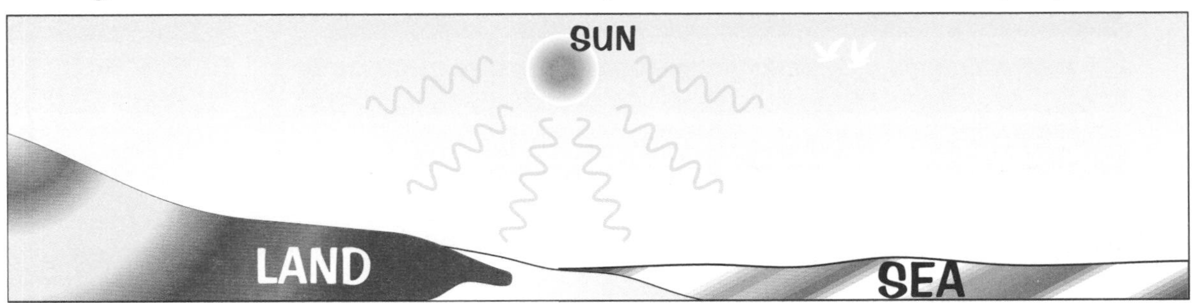

a) Decide which surface will *warm up more*, and therefore where the air will be forced to rise. Mark the surfaces **hot** and **cold** and use arrows to show where the air rises.

b) Use different arrows to show the direction of the *breezes*. Are they from the land to the sea or from the sea to the land?

Q5 *The vacuum flask has a number of features which help it to insulate its contents.* Some features are listed below, and you need to say which method *or methods* of heat transfer they are reducing. The first is done for you.

Outer cap/cup
Plastic cap filled with cork
Shiny mirrored surfaces
Vacuum
Sponge
Hot or cold liquid
Air
Plastic case

a) the cap is made of cork and plastic. ....conduction....

b) the cap seals the container. ....

c) the liquid is contained in a glass bottle. ....

d) the bottle is double walled. ....

e) the outside of each glass layer is silvered. ....

f) the inside of each glass layer is silvered. ....

g) there is a vacuum between the two walls of the glass bottle. ....

h) the bottle is surrounded by air inside the plastic case. ....

i) the bottle is supported away from the casing by insulating foam. ....

Questions on Keeping Buildings Warm

Q1 *Each of the following describe a method of keeping heat within a house.*
You need to decide the name of the insulating method and *draw a line* linking the description and the name.

Description	Name of Method
Using bits of cloth to cover up windows and doorways.	Draught Proofing
A thick layer of fibre glass wool laid over the loft floor.	Thermostatic Controls
Foam squirted into the gap between two layers of brick.	Cavity Wall Insulation
Fibre glass lagging around hot water tank.	Double Glazing
Making a window from two layers of glass instead of one.	Hot Water Tank Jacket
Using strips of foam and plastic around doors and windows.	Curtains
Controls on radiator valves to prevent overheating.	Loft Insulation

Q2 *The above energy saving ideas can have unforeseen additional benefits and problems.*

a) Double glazing reduces the amount of another form of energy *entering* the house. What is it?

....

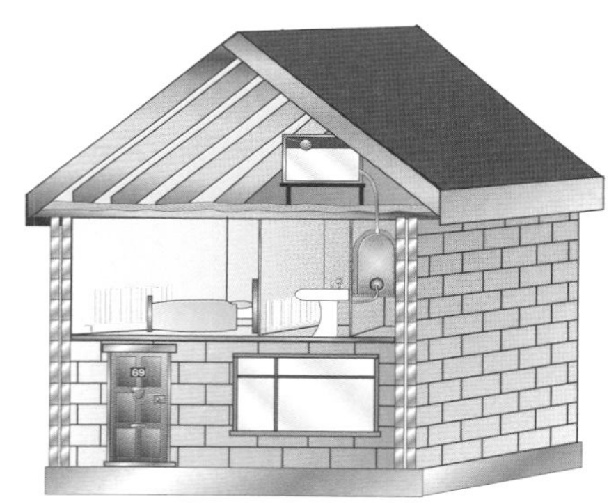

b) Draught proofing can lead to the build up a type of *dangerous gas* given off by some rocks. What is it called?

....

c) Houses with *poor ventilation* (sounds worse than 'good draught proofing') have other problems. Name *one*.

....

Q3 *Sharon and Esme have booked a winter holiday in a log cabin. Sharon thinks that wood is a good substance to keep the holiday dwellers warm.*

a) Do you agree? ....

They have a relaxing evening playing cards while it is cold and stormy outside. Esme goes up to the door. The body of the door is warm to the touch, but when she touches the brass handle, it feels very cold.

b) Explain *why* this is. ....

....

Questions on Keeping Buildings Warm

Q4 *Eric's grandmother is living in an old house which has had little attention paid to energy saving.*

Work needed	Cost of work (£)
Loft insulation	250
Hot water tank jacket	15
Double glazing	3200
Draught proofing	70
Cavity wall insulation	560
Thermostatic controls	120

As part of a science project, Eric investigates ways of saving energy in his grandmother's house, and finds out the cost of doing the work. The results are shown in the table above.

Work needed	Annual saving (£)
Loft insulation	40
Hot water tank jacket	15
Double glazing	60
Draught proofing	65
Cavity wall insulation	70
Thermostatic controls	25

Next, Eric calculates the annual saving that each piece of work would produce on his grandmother's fuel bill. He comes up with the above figures.

a) Use the figures in the *second* table to draw a bar chart.

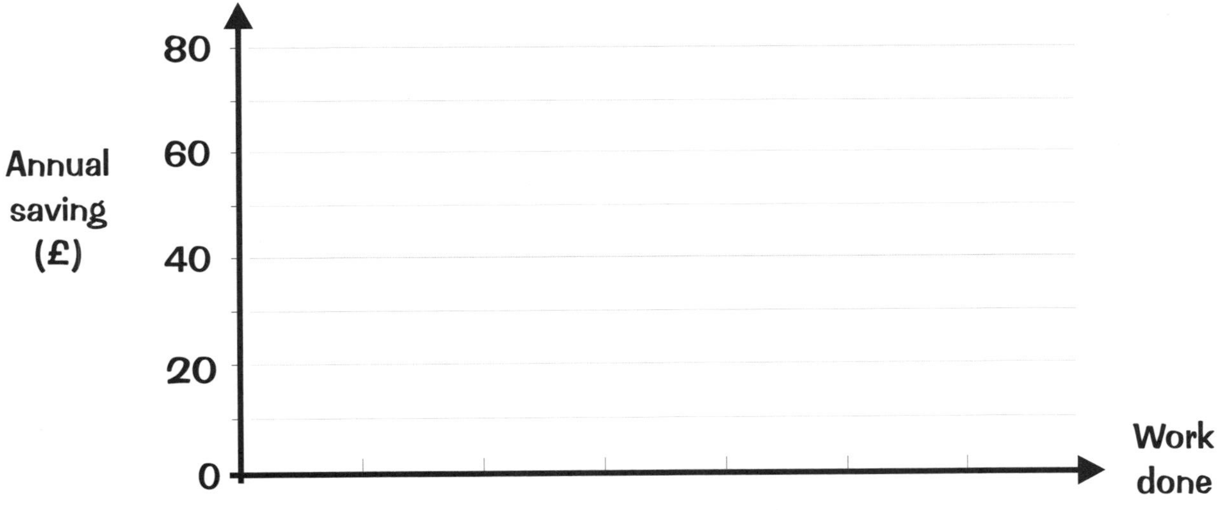

b) Which is the most *expensive* heat saving method? ....

c) Which is the *cheapest* heat saving method? ....

d) Which method saves the *most* money each year? ....

e) Which method saves the *least* money each year? ....

f) Write on each bar of your chart the *time* needed to save the cost of the work done.

g) What *other* reason, besides saving money, might there be for his frail old grandma (hint) to have some of the work done? ....

Questions on Energy Resources

Q1 *This question gives you a whole list of energy resources.*

Anagram	Energy Resource	Renewable or Non-renewable
A DOFO		
B ILO		
C EDSIT		
D DWIN		
E ARLECUN		
F LOARS		
G RUTSAAGLAN		
H ROYTHDEECLIRC		
I MISBOAS		
J ALOC		
K ESAWV		
L HOMERLAGET		

In the table:

a) *Solve* the anagrams for the energy resources in the left hand column.
b) Write down whether each resource is *renewable* or *non-renewable*.

Q2 Complete the sentences that follow. Here are the words to use.

renewable, fossil, coal, weather, sun, biomass, oil, pollution, natural gas, non-renewable

a) Name the *three* fossil fuels. ....

b) What do we call fuels that will *run out* one day? ....

c) What is the *original* energy source for lots of our energy? ....

d) If a fuel will *never* run out, we say that it is ....

e) A lot of *renewable* energy resources are unreliable because they depend on the ....

f) Non-renewable energy resources *damage* the environment due to ....

g) Fuels that have been formed from things that were *alive* long, long ago are called .... fuels.

h) Fuels that have been formed from things *recently* alive are called .... fuels.

Questions on Energy Resources

Q3 Here are some energy chains that show how some energy resources were made. You have to complete them.

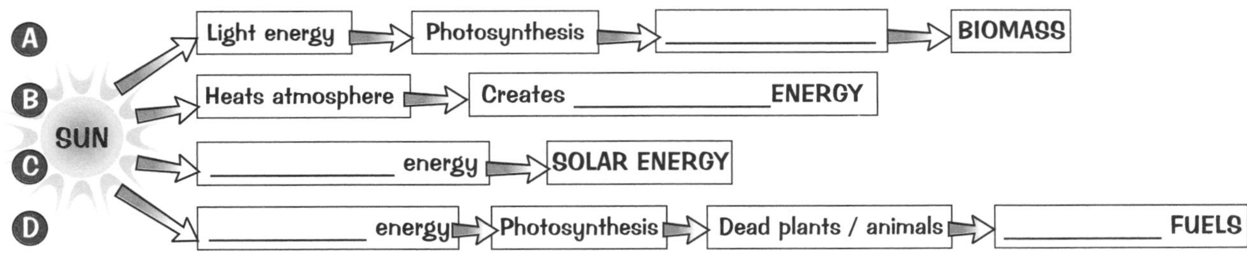

Q4 For each of the following lists, put a *ring* around the *odd one out*, and say *why* it is odd.

a) Coal, Oil, Natural Gas, Nuclear. ....

b) Wind, Wave, Geothermal, Solar. ....

c) Tidal, Biomass, Hydroelectric, Geothermal, Nuclear. ....

d) Food, Coal, Biomass, Hydroelectric, Oil. ....

e) Nuclear, Coal, Geothermal, Oil. ....

f) Solar, Biomass, Coal, Oil, Tidal. ....

Q5 *The bar chart shows the energy that was used in the U.S.A. in 1990.* Study the bar chart and answer the questions.

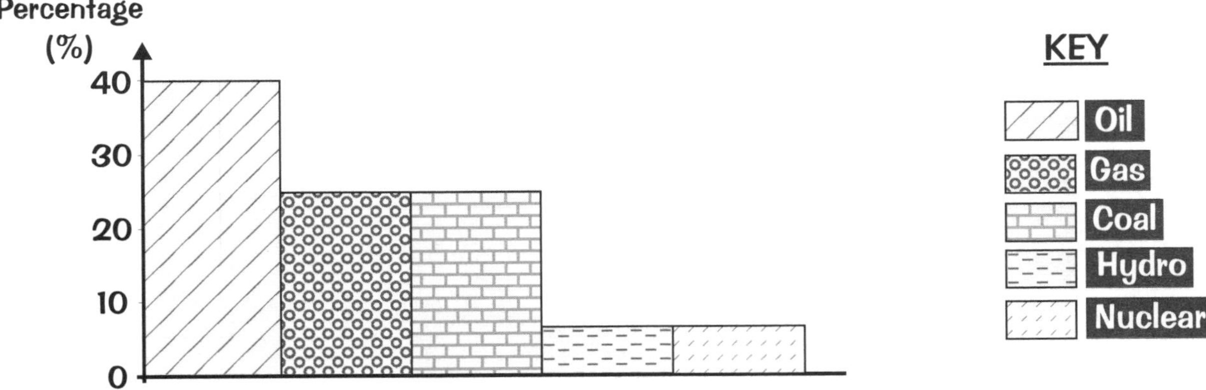

a) What *percentage* of the energy used came from oil? ....

b) How much of the energy used came from *renewable* energy? ....

c) How much of the energy used was based on *fossil fuels?* ....

d) If the chart was drawn 50 years ago, which source would *not* appear? ....

e) What do you think will have happened to the percentage of *non-renewable* energy sources used in 50 years time? ....

An Energy A-Z

Here's an Energy A to Z. Just work out the answers from the clues.

Number of Letters

A) What a car does if the forward force is bigger than the backward force.

Answer: .... (10)

B) What a ball does if it doesn't lose all its energy hitting the floor. Answer: .... (6)

C) A type of energy that gunpowder has. Answer: .... (8)

D) Energy can never be created or .... (9)

E) A type of energy that can travel down wires. Answer: .... (8)

F) To find work done, we multiply this by distance. Answer: .... (5)

G) This is a type of potential energy due to height. Answer: .... (13)

H) This is a type of energy produced by a fire. Answer: .... (4)

I) What we call energy going into a machine. Answer: .... (5)

J) We use these to measure energy in. Answer: .... (5)

K) A type of energy that moving objects have. Answer: .... (7)

L) Bright objects have this type of energy. Answer: .... (5)

M) This is something that changes energy from one type to another. Answer: .... (7)

N) The type of energy that an atom bomb has. Answer: .... (7)

O) What we call energy coming out of a machine. Answer: .... (6)

P) A squashed up jack in the box has elastic .... energy. (9)

Q) A very powerful machine does work .... (7)

R) The type of energy given off by red-hot objects. Answer: .... (7)

S) The type of energy given off by noisy objects. Answer: .... (5)

T) Another name for heat energy. Answer: .... (7)

U) The type of energy that we want machines to make a lot of. Answer: .... (6)

V) Sound energy won't travel through this. Answer: .... (6)

W) Unit that we use to measure power. Answer: .... (4)

X) Last letter of where Jack has a lot of elastic potential energy. Answer: (3)

Y) Last letter of what things need if they are to do work. Answer: .... (6)

Z) A place where animals use lots of energy. Answer: .... (3)

An Energy Resources Crossword

Use the clues to fill in the answers on this crossword. All the words are to do with Energy Resources.

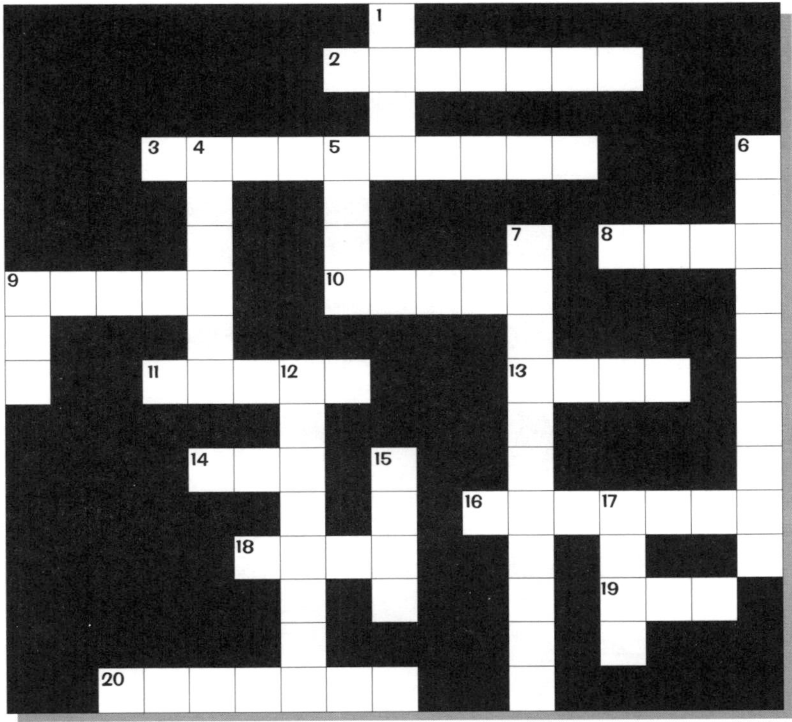

Across
2,14. A non-renewable energy resource that's not a solid or a liquid.
3. Type of renewable energy resource obtained by drilling underground
8. A good store of biomass energy.
9. Renewable energy resource that comes directly from the Sun
10. Renewable energy that relies on the Moon.
11. First part of a renewable energy resource that needs lots of rain.
13. Solid, black, non-renewable energy resource.
14. See 2 across
16. Renewable energy resource that comes from living things.
18. What happens to coal and oil in power station furnaces.
19. Non-renewable, liquid energy resource
20. Non-renewable energy resource that gives off radioactivity.

Down
1. Renewable energy resource that changes up and down movement to electricity.
4. What we need to carry out work.
5. Type of energy produced in furnaces
6. Carbon dioxide from burned fuels can cause this effect.
7. A very useful type of energy that we get from power stations.
9. What causes the energy in 9 across.
12. A store of energy that can be useful.
15. Renewable energy resource that depends on moving air
17. What causes the tides.

Questions on Power Stations

Q1 *Look at this diagram of a power station that generates electricity from a fossil fuel.* In the top row of boxes in the diagram below, fill in the **Labels** of the machinery which have been missed off, while in the bottom row of boxes, fill in the **Energy Type** involved at each stage.

Labels - **Generator, Transformer, Fuel, Turbine, Grid, Boiler.**
Energy Types - **Kinetic, Chemical, Electrical, Heat**

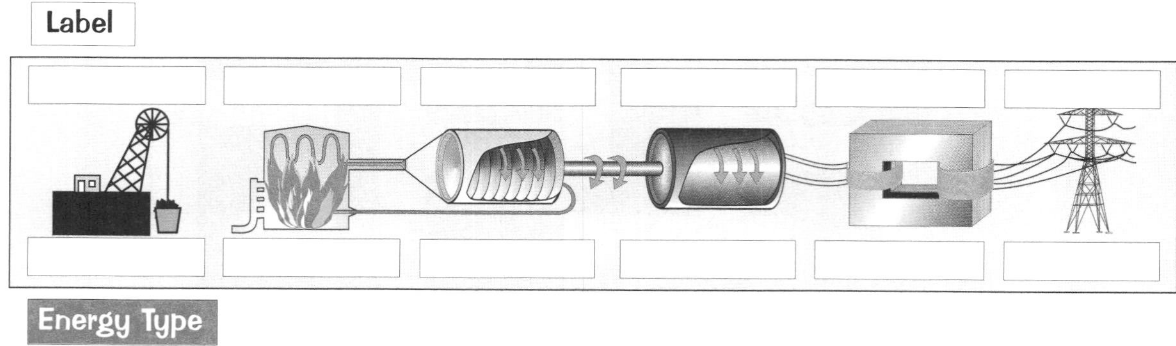

Q2 *The fuel used in an atomic power station does not have chemical energy changed to heat.*

What is the *energy change?* ....

Q3 *All energy sources have associated environmental problems, and the worst tend to be those which are non-renewable.* In this table below, put *ticks* by each environmental problem in the column(s) of the source(s) that can cause the problem.

Problem	Coal	Oil	Gas	Nuclear
Release of CO_2 (causing greenhouse effect).				
Acid rain production.				
Devastation of landscape.				
Environmental problems due to spillage at sea.				
Production of dangerous, long-lasting waste.				
Expensive plant and clean up after use.				
Danger of major catastrophe.				

Q4 Complete the following sentences by *circling* the correct answer in the brackets.

a) It's not only the fact that crude oil will one day run-out that means trouble. Crude oil is also a source of very useful **(chemicals / clean water)**. These can be used to make plastics for example.

b) We can conserve fossil fuels by using **(more / less)** energy by being efficient, and by using **(more / less)** renewable energy resources.

Questions on Wave Power and Wind Power

Q1 *One type of renewable energy resource that scientists are looking into is the wind. Here are some statements about wind energy.*

Decide whether they are *advantages* or *disadvantages* and tick the appropriate box.

Statement	Advantage	Disadvantage
A Wind turbines don't produce chemical pollution.		
B Wind turbines need lots of land.		
C Some people say wind turbines spoil the view.		
D Wind turbines don't make lots of heat.		
E They cost a lot to make.		
F They are cheap to run once they're built.		
G The wind does not always blow.		
H They need no fuel.		
I You would need 5000 wind turbines to replace a power station.		

Q2 *Another type of renewable energy resource comes from waves. This question consists of a number of statements.* Decide whether each one is *true* or *false*. Write in the space provided.

Statement	True / False
a) wave generators will be found inland	....
b) wave generators create no pollution	....
c) as waves come into shore, to water moves up and down	....
d) wave generators will not affect boat owners	....
e) we can rely on waves all of the time	....
f) here in Britain, we could make all of our electricity from wave power	....
g) the starting cost for wave generators would be high	....
h) wave generators would spoil the view	....
i) waves get bigger when the wind drops	....
j) a good place for wave generators would be a small remote island	....

Questions on Hydroelectric Power

Q1 *Hydroelectric Power depends on the Water Cycle for its energy.*

Look at this diagram of the Water Cycle, and answer the questions that follow.

a) Which letter shows *clouds?* ....

b) Which letter shows *evaporation?* ....

c) What is it that *causes* water to evaporate from the oceans?

....

d) What is the name given to the *process* of the water flowing from the mountains back to the oceans? ....

Q2 Look at the diagram of the hydroelectric station. Complete the paragraph all about hydroelectric power using the words that are provided.

environment, dam electricity, valley, rainwater, turbines, gravitational

The first step is to flood a .... that has been blocked off by a .... This traps .... which has a lot of .... potential energy. The water is let out through .... that drive generators. This makes .... The energy is generated without pollution. There is an impact on the .... and animals and plants cannot survive there.

Q3 *Here are some statements about hydroelectricity and pumped storage.* Are they *true* or *false?* Ring the correct answer.

a) Traditional power stations can be switched on and off at will. (T / F)
b) It costs a lot to build a hydroelectric station. (T / F)
c) There are fewer people using electricity at night so it is cheaper. (T / F)
d) Hydroelectric power stations make the same amount of electricity all the time. (T / F)
e) Water only ever flows downwards through a pumped storage system. (T / F)
f) Pumped storage systems use electricity from normal stations to pump water. (T / F)
g) Hydroelectric stations do not produce polluting gases. (T / F)
h) Hydroelectric stations have no impact on animals and plants. (T / F)
i) Pumped storage is just a way of storing energy for later (T / F)

Questions on Tidal and Geothermal Energy

Q1 Some of these statements apply to geothermal energy, and some apply to tidal energy. Others have nothing to do with either.

Try to work out which is which, and put a *tick* in the correct column.

Statement	Geothermal	Tidal	Neither
A Heat that comes from underground.			
B Works because of the attraction of the moon.			
C Water turns to steam as it is pumped through the Earth.			
D Produces carbon dioxide pollution.			
E Water flows through turbines.			
F The Earth's crust needs to be quite thin nearby.			
G The power generated depends on the time of year.			
H Relies on radioactive decay of substances.			
I Can produce all the electricity we need.			

Q2 Complete the words that answer each of the clues that are all to do with *tidal* and *geothermal* power.

a) Radioactive decay of this element makes the heat for geothermal power. U.......................

b) The force produced by this pulls the water to make tides. M...............................

c) This is what could block up a river mouth if a tidal barrage is built. S............................

d) This is the name of the force that pulls the water into tides. G...............................

e) This is the main cost of getting power from geothermal energy. D...............................

f) This is what we call the mouth of a river where we could generate tidal power. E..................

g) This is how many times a day you get a high tide. T...............................

Q3 *Look at these two diagrams. One shows geothermal power, the other is for tidal power.*

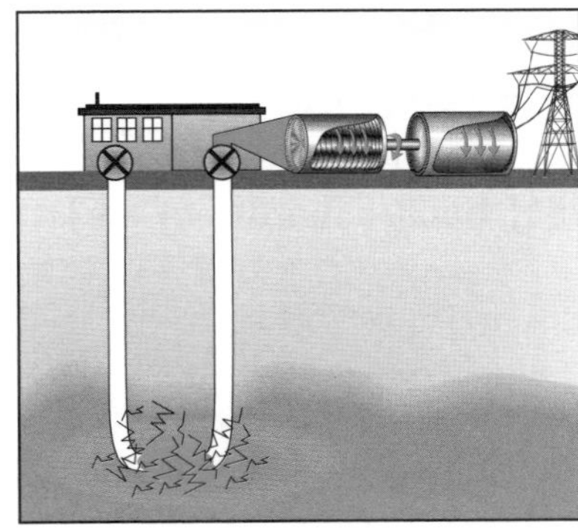

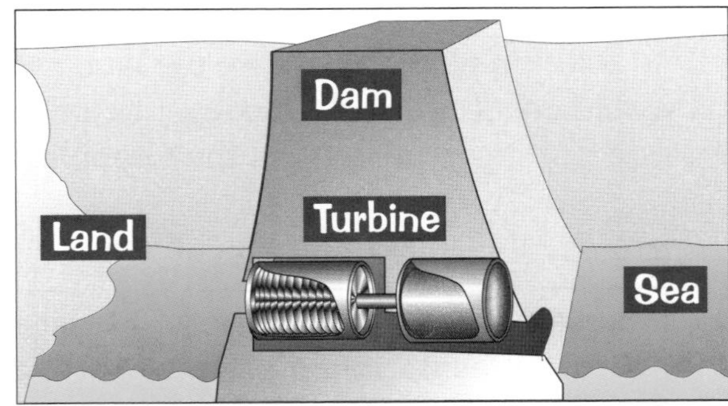

a) Add colour to the diagram for geothermal power, showing where the water is *cold*, and where it is *hot*.

b) The diagram for tidal power shows the water level at low tide. Show where the water level could be for *high tide*.

c) Add an arrow to the tidal power diagram showing which *direction* the water flows after the tide has gone out.

Questions on Solar Energy and Biomass

Q1 These sentences are all about solar energy. Read them and fill in the missing gaps using the words in the box below..

high, furnace, three, unreliable, pollution, cell, black, panel

a) There are .... ways of getting the energy from sunlight.

b) A solar .... changes the energy into electricity immediately.

c) A solar .... absorbs the sunlight to heat water in pipes.

d) A solar .... focuses the Sun's rays to turn water into steam to drive turbines.

e) None of these methods directly creates any ....

f) To absorb the Sun's energy well, the best colour is ....

g) The costs to start using solar energy are ....

h) In Britain, solar energy would be ....

Q2 Think about using biomass, or living things to make electricity. One way could be to use trees. Look at the sentences and *ring* the correct option in each sentence.

a) Trees get their energy from the **(Sun / soil)**.
b) They absorb energy with their **(trunks / leaves)**.
c) The process is called **(photosynthesis / combustion)**.
d) They take in **(carbon dioxide / nitrogen)**.
e) They give out **(sulphur dioxide / oxygen)**.
f) Their energy is released by us through **(rotting / burning)**.
g) Water would be turned into **(steam / ice)**.
h) It would be used to drive **(turbines / oscillators)**.
i) A big drawback would be the amount of **(land / water)** that would be used up.
j) One solution would be to use the land for **(buildings / leisure)**.
k) It would cost **(nothing / money)** to harvest and process the wood.
l) Wood burning would affect the Greenhouse Effect **(badly / hardly at all)**.

Q3 *Rearrange* the stages in the generation of electricity from wood burning.

harvest trees, burn in boiler furnace, grow fast growing trees, generate steam, chop up trees, generate electricity, power turbine

....

....

....

An Electricity Generation A-Z

Solve the clues to complete this Electricity generation A to Z. (X and Z are missing)

A)	Little pollution from renewable energy resources. A real	(9)
B)	Type of renewable energy source based on living things. Answer:	(7)
C)	Non-renewable energy resource. Black, solid, fossil fuel. Answer:	(4)
D)	This is a small example that does the same as a generator in a power station. Answer:	(6)
E)	A very useful type of energy that people work hard to generate. Answer:	(11)
F)	This is a substance that can be burned to give out heat. Answer:	(4)
G)	The word for making electricity. Answer:	(8)
H)	A type of energy resource that we get from gathering water high in mountains. Answer:	(13)
I)	What we wrap around houses to keep them warm and to save resources. Answer:	(10)
J)	The unit that we use to measure energy. Answer:	(5)
K)	The type of energy that the moving wind has. Answer:	(7)
L)	A wind power station will need a big area of this. Answer:	(4)
M)	Big examples of these are found in power stations to help make electricity. Answer:	(7)
N)	This type of gas is an example of a fossil fuel. Answer:	(7)
O)	This black liquid is a fossil fuel that can cause pollution. Answer:	(3)
P)	This is a type of station that produces electricity. Answer:	(5)
Q)	Non-renewable energy resources are running out	(7)
R)	A type of energy resource that will never run out. Answer:	(9)
S)	The type of power that comes directly from the Sun. Answer:	(5)
T)	The type of power that relies on the gravity of the Moon. Answer:	(5)
U)	A fuel used in nuclear power stations. Answer:	(7)
V)	Crude oil can be used to make chemicals that are	(8)
W)	An energy source that we can extract from the sea. Answer:	(4)
Y)	These boats rely on wind power to move them around. Answer:	(6)

A Question about Yo-yos

Q1 *As you know by now, energy and energy changes are involved in loads of things. And here's one you might be familiar with.*

a) There are *three* forms of energy in a falling yo-yo. Rotational energy is one. What are the other *two?*

....

....

If you let a yo-yo fall from your hand it won't return all the way back up because it loses energy as it rubs against the string.

b) What *type* of energy is it losing by doing this?

....

c) Normally, we want a yo-yo to return to our hand and for this to happen we must give the yo-yo energy. Give *one example* of how this could be done.

....

....

It is possible to work out how much of the yo-yos energy is lost through friction. We do this (rather strangely you might think) by calculating the gravitational potential energy of the yo-yo before it is released from the hand and again after it has risen back up to the point below the hand where it stops (assuming it is given no energy).

We calculate potential energy before the yo-yo is released.....

....and again after it has returned back up the string.

d) If Potential Energy at Start = 0.425J and Potential Energy After Returning Up String = 0.3J, work out the Energy Lost by subtracting one value from another.

Energy Lost = ...

e) Given that : Percentage Potential Energy Lost = $\frac{\text{Potential Energy Lost}}{\text{Potential Energy at Start}} \times 100$

work out the Percentage Potential Energy Lost for the yo-yo.

....

This value is also the percentage of energy the yo-yo loses through friction, ie rubbing against the string. Quite a bit isn't it?

Pictorial Energy Wordsearch

All the clues to this wordsearch are in the pictures below. All you have to do is find the missing word in each of the sentences and work out the names of the things the arrows are pointing to. The number of letters in each case is given by the number in the circle.

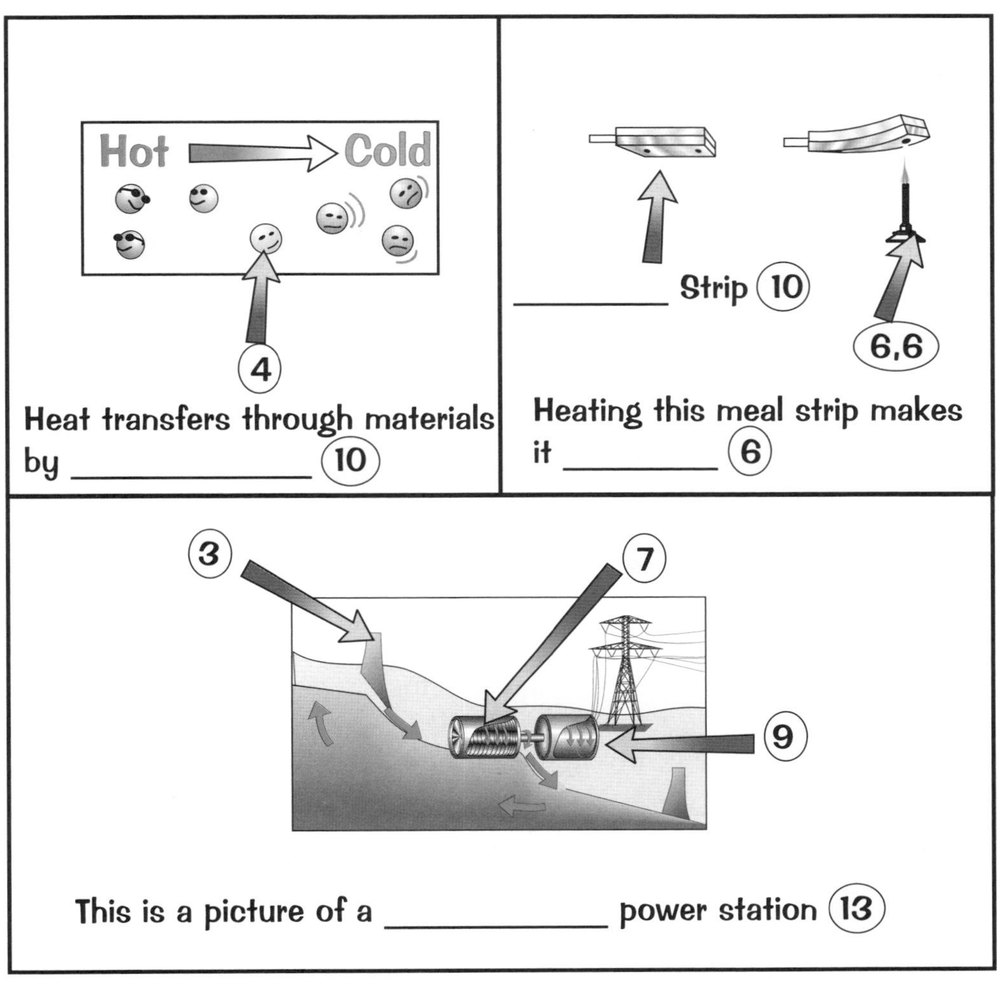

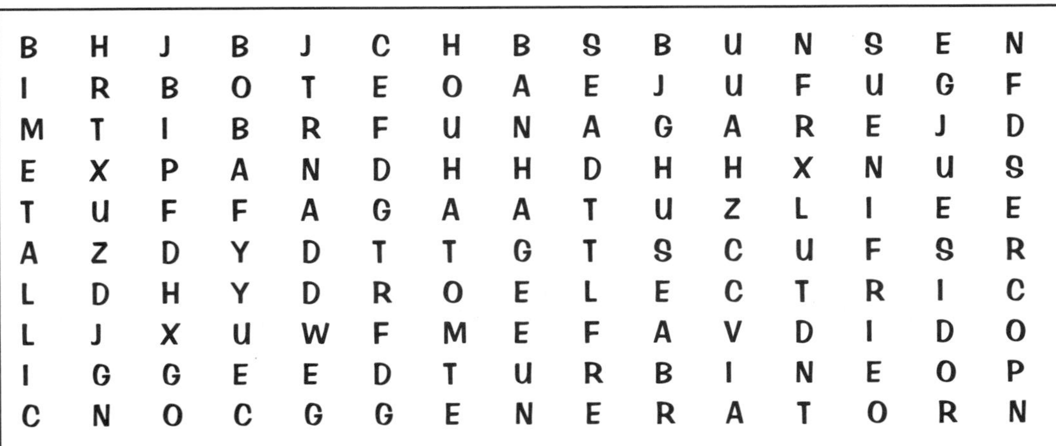

B	H	J	B	J	C	H	B	S	B	U	N	S	E	N
I	R	B	O	T	E	O	A	E	J	U	F	U	G	F
M	T	I	B	R	F	U	N	A	G	A	R	E	J	D
E	X	P	A	N	D	H	H	D	H	H	X	N	U	S
T	U	F	F	A	G	A	A	T	U	Z	L	I	E	E
A	Z	D	Y	D	T	T	G	T	S	C	U	F	S	R
L	D	H	Y	D	R	O	E	L	E	C	T	R	I	C
L	J	X	U	W	F	M	E	F	A	V	D	I	D	O
I	G	G	E	E	D	T	U	R	B	I	N	E	O	P
C	N	O	C	G	G	E	N	E	R	A	T	O	R	N

Questions on Atomic Structure

Q1 *The diagram below shows the particles that constitute an atom.*

Complete the labels in the diagram.

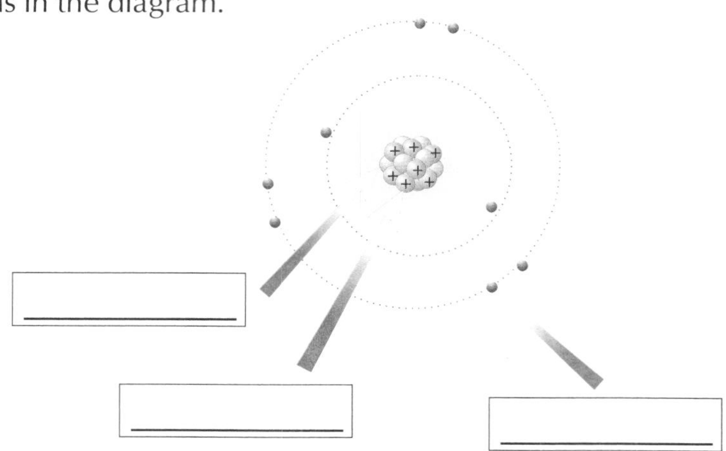

Q2 Complete these two paragraphs about atomic structure using the words from the boxes:

nucleus	electrons	protons	neutrons	mass	volume

a) All atoms are made up of a .... and a number of .... The .... is made up of .... and neutrons. The .... have a positive charge and the .... are electrically neutral. Most of the atom's .... is in the nucleus, but it takes up a relatively small ....

electrons	nucleus	small	1/2000	proton	neutron	identical

b) The .... orbit the .... They carry a negative charge (and are really really ....). The ratio of the mass of an electron to the mass of a proton or neutron is about .... The masses of the .... and the proton are almost ....

Q3 Complete the following tables about the particles that make up atoms.

Particle	Relative Mass
	1
	1
	1/2000

Particle	Electric charge (positive/negative/neutral)	Size of Electric charge
Neutron		
Proton	positive	
Electron		-1

Questions on Atomic Structure

Q4 Complete the blanks in the table below.

Element	Atomic Number	Mass Number	Number of protons	Number of electrons	Number of neutrons
Helium	2	4			
Carbon	6	12			
Oxygen			8		8
Neon			10		10
Sodium				11	12
Magnesium	12	24			
Chlorine				17	18
Calcium		40	20		

Q5 *Copy and complete* the following paragraph about isotopes using the words in the box. You may use a word more than once:

atomic	mass	alpha	neutrons	electrons
stable	beta	three	element	protons

Isotopes of the same .... have equal numbers of .... and .... but different numbers of .... Hence they have the same .... number but a different .... number. Every .... has at least .... different isotopes but usually only one or two .... ones. If a radioactive isotope decays, radiation is emitted. If an .... or a .... particle is emitted then a different .... is formed.

Q6 Information about six atoms A, B, C, D, E and F is given below.

Atom A: 8 neutrons, mass number 16	Atom D: 6 neutrons, mass number 11
Atom B: 3 electrons, mass number 7	Atom E: 3 neutrons, mass number 6
Atom C: 8 protons, mass number 17	Atom F: 6 protons, mass number 12

For which three atoms do you not need the mass number to identify the element?

....

Questions on Radiation

Q1 *The diagrams below show alpha, beta and gamma radiation being fired at a line of four obstacles: thin mica, a hand, thin aluminium and thick lead.*

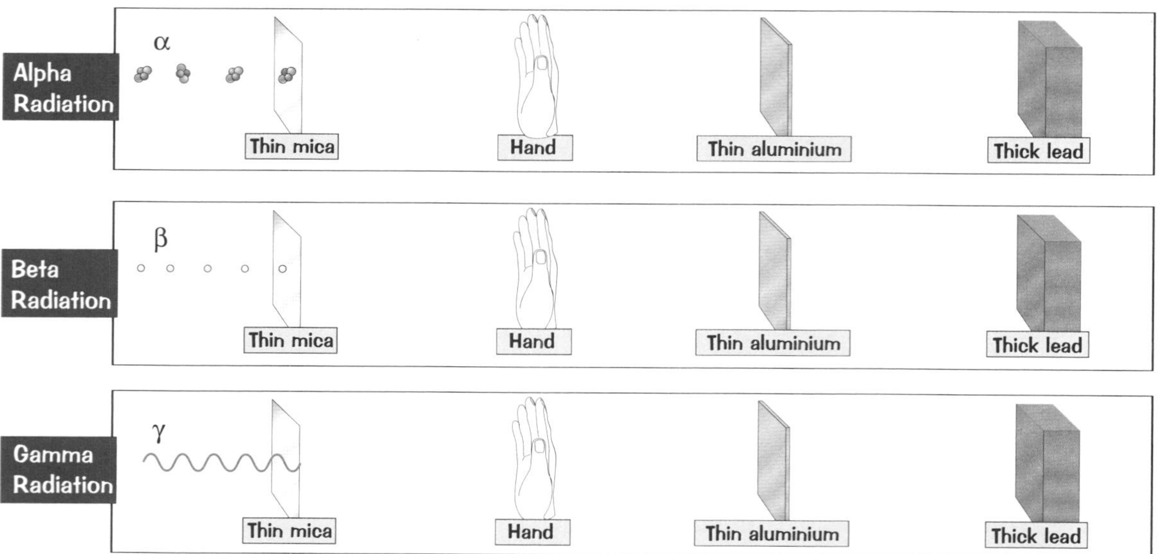

a) On each diagram *draw the path* of the radiation before it is absorbed.

b) Give a reason why alpha particles only penetrate a *short distance* into a material.

Reason: ....

....

c) Give a reason why gamma radiation is used in hospitals to treat cancer patients.

Reason: ....

....

Q2 Fill in the table below using the phrases in the box:

electromagnetic waves | electron | γ | charge = –1
mass number = 4 | α | zero mass | helium nucleus | β

Alpha particle	Beta particle	Gamma radiation

Questions on Radiation

Q3 Read the information in the following table, then answer the questions after it.

> *Alpha:* Streams of helium nuclei. Easily stopped — cannot go through paper or skin. Harmful only if swallowed or if they enter the body through a break in the skin. Slow and heavy compared to beta and gamma radiation.
> *Beta:* Streams of electrons. More penetrating, but can be stopped by thin metal sheet. They travel at high speed — lighter and faster then alpha particles.
> *Gamma:* A more energetic form of energy than even light. Very penetrating — can only be stopped by thick lead, steel or concrete.

a) Which radiation is the most penetrating? ....

b) Which radiation is the least penetrating? ....

c) Which travels at the speed of light and is a form of energy? ....

d) Which radiation is a stream of helium nuclei? ....

e) Which is a stream of electrons? ....

f) Which radiation is the slowest? ....

g) Which is not very harmful unless the source is inside the body? ....

Q4 *A cereal company wants to check the level of 'pop rice' in each box of cereal they produce. They can do this by passing the boxes between a radioactive source and a detector.*

a) Name a suitable detector. ....

b) *The company choose a radioactive source that emits beta particles.*

i) Why should an alpha source not be used? ....

....

ii) Why should a gamma source not be used? ....

....

c) Give two safety precautions that should be taken by the technician who has to put the radioactive source in place.

1. ....

2. ....

Questions on Radioactive Materials

Q1 *Complete* the following sentences about radiation and food, using the words in the box.

irradiation	dose	surgical	temperatures	radioactive	sterilise	gamma
instruments	damage	exposed	microbes	fresh	safe	source

A high dose of .... radiation can be used to .... food, keeping it .... for longer. The process kills harmful ...., but does less .... to food than treatments like boiling that involve exposure to high .... The food is not .... afterwards, so it is perfectly .... to eat. The isotope needs to be a very pure .... of gamma rays. This method can also be used to sterilise ....

Q2 After the sentences a) to g), write down the *correct word or phrase* from the box below:

carbon-14	heat	half-life	radioactive decay	chain reaction	uranium	electricity

a) Used as a nuclear fuel. ....

b) Time taken for a sample's count rate to drop by one half. ....

c) Process by which energy is generated in a nuclear fuel. ....

d) Used for finding out how long ago plants and animals died. ....

e) Form of energy leaving a nuclear power station. ....

f) Responsible for much of the heat inside the Earth. ....

Q3 *The table below gives information about four radioactive isotopes.*

Isotope	Half life	Type of radiation given out
$^{231}_{90}Th$	1 day	beta
$^{227}_{90}Th$	18 days	alpha
$^{227}_{89}Ac$	22 years	beta
$^{231}_{91}Pa$	32,000 years	alpha

Choose which isotope would be the best choice for monitoring the thickness of paper.

Isotope: ....

Explanation: ....

....

....

....

Questions on Radioactive Materials

Q4 *The diagram below shows how a radiation source can be used to keep a metal sheet at a constant thickness.*

a) Complete the labels around the diagram with these words:

rollers
gamma radiation
hydraulic control
radiation detector
radiation source

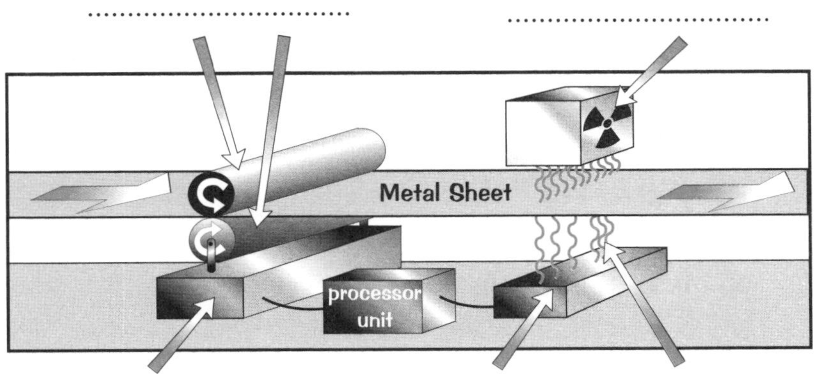

b) The radioactive isotope used here must have a *long half-life*. What would happen if the half-life was very short? ....

....

c) What *type of radiation* would you choose if you wanted to monitor the thickness of cardboard? ....

d) Explain why gamma radiation would be the *wrong* choice of radiation in c).

....

....

Q5 *Complete* the table summarising the uses of radioactive isotopes.

Use of radioactive isotope	Is it best to use an ALPHA, BETA or GAMMA emitter?	Should the isotope have a SHORT, MEDIUM or LONG half-life?
Tracers in medicine		
Detecting leaks in pipes		
Sterilisation of food		
Thickness control (paper)		
Thickness control (metal sheets)		

Questions on Half-Life

Q1 *Complete* the following sentences about radioactive half-life, using the words in the box:

zero	long	time	half	atoms	radioactivity	decay
gamma	alpha	beta	short	random	nucleus	decreases

The .... of a sample always .... over time. Each time a decay occurs, ..., ... or .... radiation is emitted. This means a radioactive .... has decayed. Since radioactivity is a .... process, the level of activity of a sample may never reach ....

Half-life is the .... taken for .... of the radioactive .... now present to .... An isotope with a .... half-life decays more quickly than an isotope with a .... half-life.

Q2 The count rate of the radioactive material iodine-131 was measured. Here are the results:

Count rate in counts per second	280	200	140	99
Time in days	0	4	8	12

a) Plot the graph on the paper provided opposite.

b) *The half-life of iodine-131 is the time taken for the count rate to halve.*

How many days is the half-life of iodine-131?

....

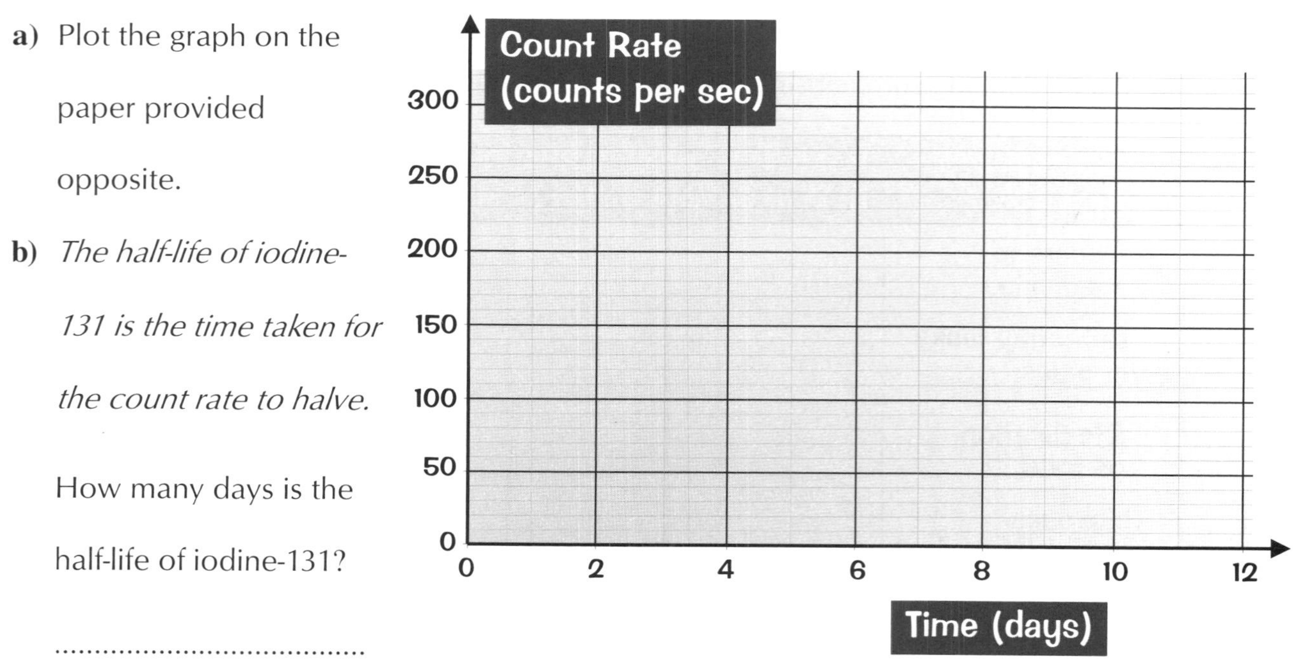

Questions on Half-Life

Q3 *Fill in the gaps* in the paragraph below, using the words in the box.

decays	living	constant	die	amount	long

Carbon-14 is a radioactive isotope of carbon and it is found in the carbon dioxide of the air. The amount stays fairly .... in the air. The same proportion of carbon-14 is also found in .... things. However, when they ...., the carbon-14 is trapped and it gradually .... By simply measuring the .... of carbon-14 found in the item, you can easily calculate how .... ago the item was .... material, because it takes 5,600 years for the activity to fall by half.

Q4 *When Lead-210 (atomic number 82) decays it gives out a beta particle and Bismuth-210 is formed. This decays with the emission of a beta particle to form Polonium-210.*

a) *The graph opposite shows how the activity of bismuth-210 varies with time.*

By looking at the graph, *estimate* the half-life of bismuth-210.

Half-life: ....

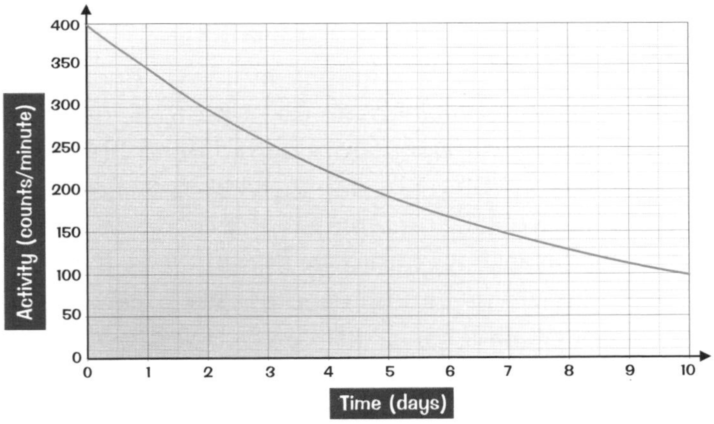

Activity (counts/minute): 0, 50, 100, 150, 200, 250, 300, 350, 400

Time (days): 0, 1, 2, 3, 4, 5, 6, 7, 8, 9, 10

b) In bismuth-210, what does the "210" represent? ....

c) *Polonium-210 decays with the emission of an alpha particle. An isotope of lead is formed.*

What is the *mass number* of this isotope of lead? ....

d) When a radioactive atom decays, what part of the atom is decaying?

....

e) What piece of equipment could be used to measure the count rate of an isotope?

....

A Radioactivity Crossword

Use the clues to fill in the answers to the crossword.

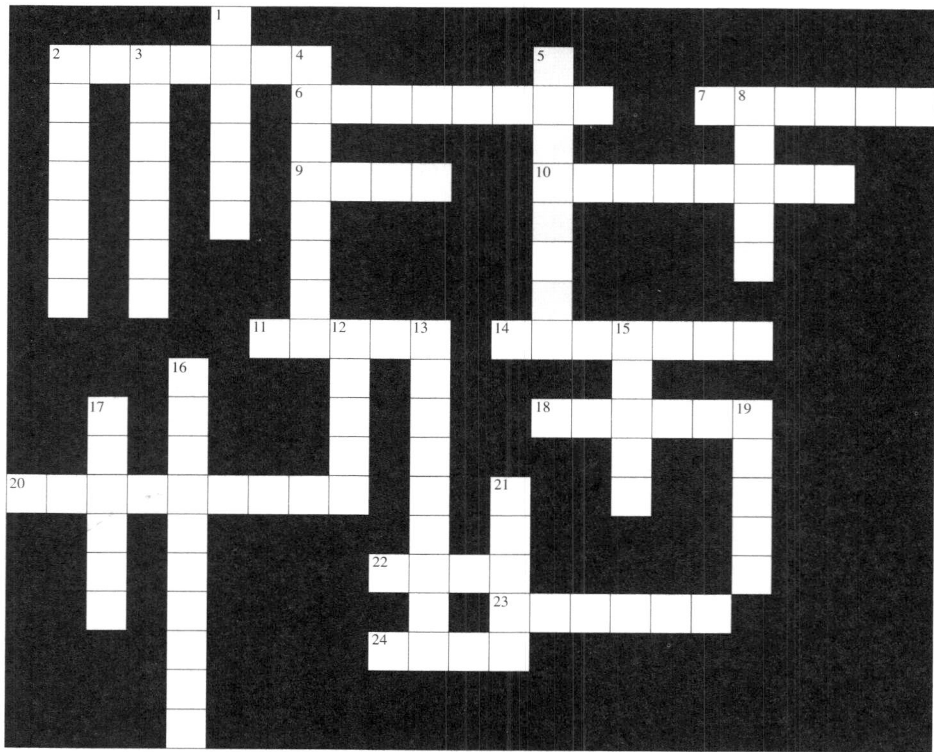

Across

2. A particle with no charge found in an atom. (7)
6. A negatively charged particle orbiting an atom. (8)
7. You never know when an atom will decay because radioactivity is a .... process. (6)
9. A mighty particle made up of protons, neutrons and electrons. (4)
10. Forms of the same atom with different numbers of neutrons. (8)
11. These can be really damaged by radiation. (5)
14. What we call something with no charge, like a neutron or an atom. (7)
18. This disease is caused by mutant cells. (6)
20. Radioactivity can be used to check the .... of a sheet of material. (9)
22. Photographic .... can be used to detect radioactivity. (4)
23. Second part of name of tube used to detect radiation in the laboratory. (6)
24. Sort of radiation that is made of high energy electrons. (4)

Down

1. Positively charged particle found in the nucleus. (6)
2. Where all the protons and neutrons are found. Also the control centre of a cell in biology. (7)
3. A radioactive substance that's used in power stations. (7)
4. The type of charge on an electron and a beta particle. (8)
5. The type of charge on a proton or a nucleus. (8)
8. Heavy type of radioactive particle. (5)
12. Radiation can be used to check for these in pipes. (5)
13. Radiation can do this to food and surgical instruments. (9)
15. Your teacher needs these to handle radioactive substances. (5)
16. Type of radiation that's there all the time. (10)
17. First part of name of tube used to detect radiation in the laboratory. (6)
19. Radioactive gas that comes out of rocks. (5)
21. Type of radiation with no mass and no charge. (5)

Radioactivity Match-up

This page contains a number of TERMS and DEFINITIONS.

Match each definition to the correct term by drawing arrows between the boxes:

TERMS	DEFINITIONS
GEIGER-MULLER TUBE	caused by changes to the nuclei of atoms
RADIOACTIVITY	apparatus used to study radiation in the laboratory
PROTON	radioactive wave that has no mass or charge
MASS NUMBER	radiation that's there all the time
ALPHA	negatively charged particle that orbits the nucleus
BACKGROUND	positively charged particle found in nucleus
BETA	heavy, positive radioactive particle
ELECTRON	radioactivity is this sort of process
ATOMIC NUMBER	the total number of protons and neutrons in the nucleus
GAMMA	the bit at the centre of an atom
NUCLEUS	particle from nucleus that has no charge
RANDOM	the number telling us how many protons there are in the nucleus
NEUTRON	these radioactive particles are high energy electrons

Questions on Radiation Hazards

Q1 Complete the following sentences on the dangers of radioactive particles. Fill in the gaps using the words in the boxes:

damage	mass	ionised	atoms	beta	damaging	molecules	alpha	charge

Radioactive particles can be very .... to living cells. Alpha, beta and gamma radiation can all cause ...., though .... and .... particles are generally more damaging because they have .... and .... For damage to occur, ... and .... in living tissue must be .... by the radiation.

killing	mutant	DNA	sickness	exposed	cancer
mutated	controls	radiation	division	dose	nucleus

The part of the cell that .... what the cell does is called the .... This contains the ...., which is essential to the cell. If this is damaged, we say that the cell has ...., or that it is a .... cell. This can sometimes lead to uncontrolled .... of the cell, a condition known as .... Sometimes acute illness can occur when somebody is .... to a very large .... of radiation. This is called .... and is caused by the radiation .... off cells.

Q2 *The damage done by radiation depends on the type of radiation a person is exposed to, and where the source is in relation to the body.*

a) Which type(s) of radiation are most dangerous *outside* the body? ....

Why is this? ....

....

b) Which type(s) of radiation are most dangerous *inside* the body? ....

Why is this? ....

....

Questions on Radiation Hazards

Q3 *Below are some rules that your teacher will follow when handling radioactive materials in the laboratory.* Fill in the gaps using the words in the box:

soon	far	skin	lead	arm's	looking	away	tongs	back

a) Never allow the source to come into contact with your .... The sources should always be handled with ....

b) Keep the source as .... from the body as possible. Hold it at .... length if possible.

c) Point the source .... from the body. Avoid .... directly at the source.

d) Keep the source in a .... box. When the experiment is over, put .... the source as .... as possible.

Q4 Below is a list of precautions that should be taken by people who work with radiation. Draw arrows between the boxes to match the correct reason to each precaution:

PRECAUTIONS	REASONS
Use a protective suit if you work with radioactivity in industry.	Mutant cells cause cancer which can be very dangerous.
If you are pregnant, you should not work with radiation.	Radiation can do a lot of damage inside the body.
Get treatment immediately if you swallow or breathe in radioactive material.	The suit stops you breathing in particles or getting them stuck on your skin.
See a doctor if you get an unusual patch on your skin.	Radiation is very damaging for growing animals and humans.
Point radioactive sources away from you.	Where the radiation is very strong, it can even get through lead.
Do not look directly at a radioactive source.	Radiation travels in almost straight lines.
Use a remotely controlled robot in some situations.	Lots of radiation is slowed down or stopped by lead.
Keep radioactive elements in a lead box.	The covering of the eye is quite thin and radiation could get in easily.

Questions on Nuclear Fission

Q1 *Most of the nuclear reactors in the UK rely on the nuclear fission of uranium fuel. This reaction can be represented by the following equation.*

$$^{235}_{92}U + ^{1}_{0}n \rightarrow ^{90}_{36}Kr + ^{143}_{56}Ba + 3(^{1}_{0}n)$$

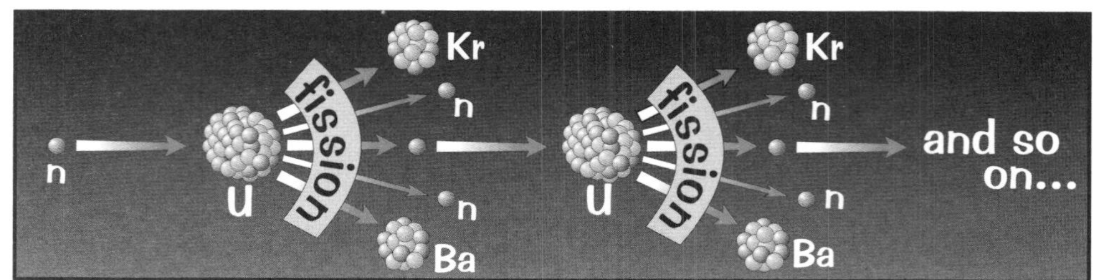

Use the equation above to answer the following questions:

a) How many protons are there in the nucleus of a uranium-235 atom? ....

b) How many neutrons are there in the nucleus of a uranium-235 atom? ....

c) How many protons in total are there on each side? ....

d) How many neutrons are there in total on each side? ....

e) How many free neutrons are there to start with? ....

f) How many are there after the first reaction? ....

g) If all these cause further fission, how many will there be next? ....

h) Complete the table to show how quickly the number of neutrons increases if they all go on to cause further fission:

Turn	0	1	2	3	4	5	6	7	8
Number	1	3							

i) Why is this called a chain reaction? ....

....

j) What can happen if the reaction is allowed to get out of control like this?

....

....

Questions on Nuclear Equations

Q2 Complete the table below. It will help you in working out these nuclear equations.

Radiation	Mass Number	Atomic Number	Charge
alpha			
beta			
gamma			

Q3 *This question concerns the changes in an atom when a substance emits an alpha particle.*

a) Draw a picture in the box opposite to show the particles in an alpha particle. Use different colours for the protons and neutrons.

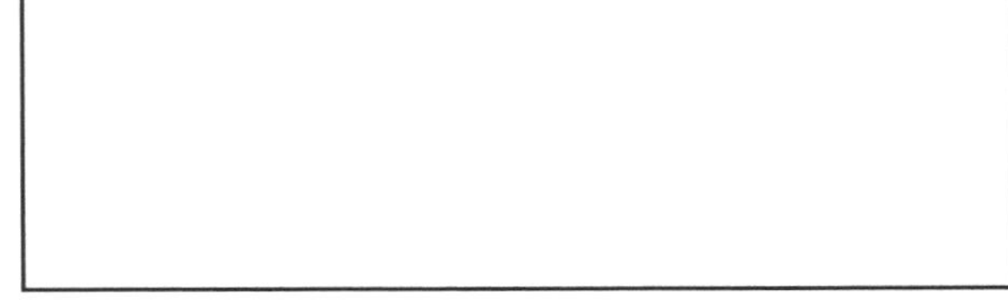

b) The atom that we are going to think about is an imaginary one, cogium. The symbol for the atom is $^{20}_{8}Cg$. Here is a picture of the nucleus of a cogium atom:

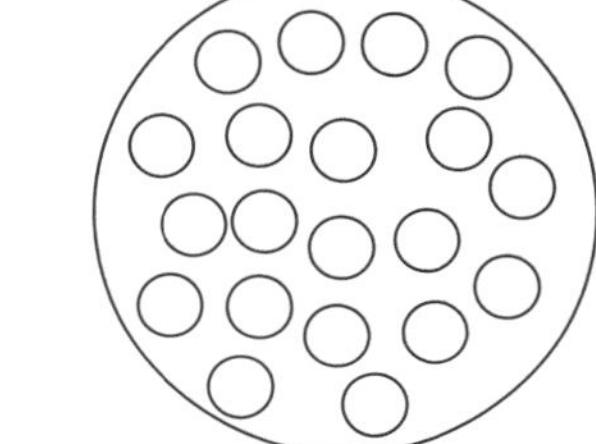

Colour in the particles using the same colours that you used for the alpha particle in part a).

c) Now colour this diagram to showing a cogium atom emitting an alpha particle:

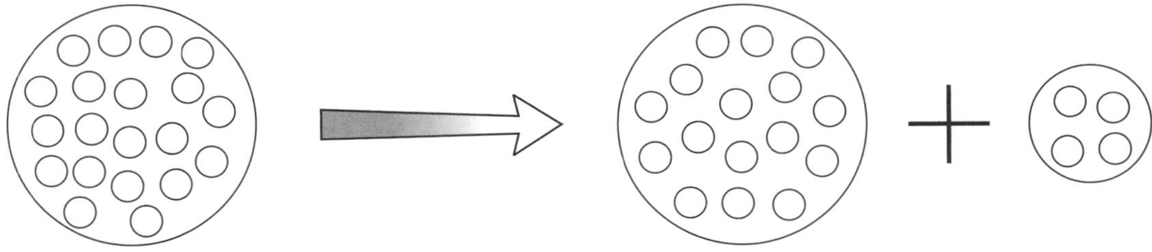

d) What will be the atomic number of the atom you're left with? ....

e) What will be the mass number of the atom you're left with? ....

Q4 Complete the table to show what happens to the mass number and atomic number of a nucleus that emits these radioactive particles:

Particle emitted	How does the mass number change?	How does the atomic number change?
Alpha		
Beta		
Gamma		

General Certificate of Secondary Education

Science: Double Award (Co-ordinated and Modular)

Foundation Paper: Trial Examination

Monday 7 June 1999 9.30 am — 11.00 am

Centre name										
Centre number						Candidate number				
Surname										
Other names										

In addition to this paper you will need
- Calculator
- Pencil
- Protractor

Time
- 1 hour 30 minutes.

Instructions to candidates
- Write your name and other details in the spaces provided above.
- Answer **all** the questions in this paper.
- Write your answers in this combined question paper/answer book.
- Write your answers in blue or black ink or ballpoint pen.
- Do all rough work on the paper.

Information for candidates
- The number of marks is given in brackets at the end of each question or part-question.
- Marks will not be deducted for incorrect answers.
- You are reminded of the need for good English and clear presentation.
- In calculations show clearly how you work out your answers.

For examiner's use	
Page 143	
144	
145	
146	
147	
148	
149	
150	
151	
152	
153	
154	
Total	

Leave margin blank

1) A skier is travelling over an area where the snow is fresh and not packed down. He comes to a halt and rests. The skis stay on the top of the snow, sinking in just a bit. The skier wants to take a photograph, and not thinking very clearly, clips his boots out of the skis and steps sideways.

a) Describe what will happen when the skier steps on to the snow.

....

(1 mark)

b) Use scientific ideas to explain what will happen.

....

....

....

....

(4 marks)

The skier continues down the slope and gets to the bottom. Here there is a lift waiting to go back up to the top. The lift has a length of 840m, and rises through a height of 240m. The skier is taken up to the top of the slope in 2 minutes.

c) Calculate the average speed of the skier going up the lift. Show clearly how you get your answer, and give the correct unit.

....

....

....

....

(3 marks)

d) Complete the following sentence.

On Earth the gravitational field strength is about .... N/kg.

(1 mark)

The mass of the skier is 70kg.

e) Use the equation below to calculate the weight of the skier.

Weight (N) = Mass (kg) × gravitational field strength (N/kg)

f) Calculate the useful work done by the motor pulling the skier to the top of the slope.

....

....

(2 marks)

g) Why is the actual energy consumed going to be larger than the answer you calculated in part f)?

....

....

(2 mark)

2) The diagram shows an attempt to lift a heavy stone with a strong lever. (The mass of the lever is negligible.)

The stone has a mass of 350kg.

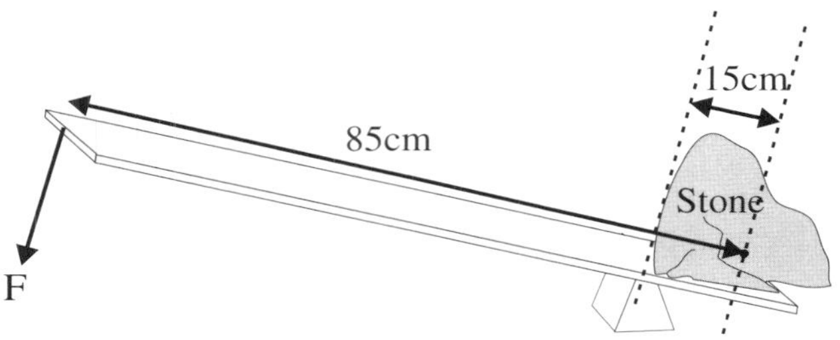

a) Use the equation below to calculate the force F needed to just lift the stone. Take g = 10 N/kg.

Weight (N) = Mass (kg) × gravitational field strength (N/kg)

....

....

(2 marks)

b) Give two further uses of levers in everyday life.

1) ....

(1 mark)

2) ....

(1 mark)

3) The diagram shows a Thermos flask (see opposite).

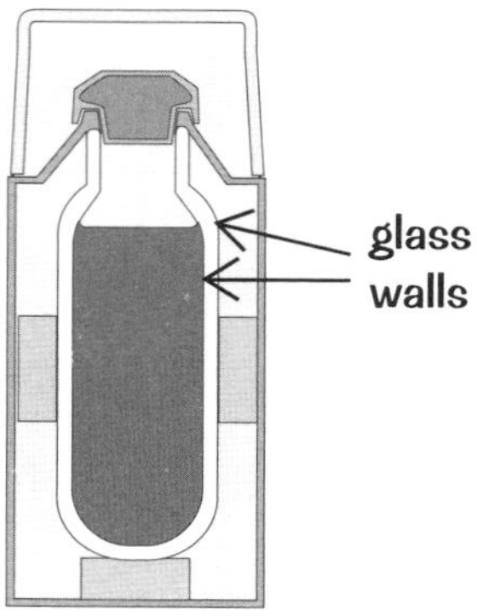

a) There is a narrow space between the two glass walls of the flask. What is contained here?

....

(1 mark)

b) What is the only method of heat transfer that can occur through here?

....

(1 mark)

c) Both the inner and outer walls are coated in shiny metal. What method of heat transfer is reduced by this coating?

....

(1 mark)

d) Explain your answer to part c).

....

....

(2 marks)

e) Give a suitable material for making the cap, and explain your choice.

....

....

....

(2 marks)

f) Why is a cap very important for the Thermos flask?

....

(1 mark)

Leave margin blank

4) A set of readings of voltage and current are taken for a component R. They are shown in the table opposite.

V (V)	I (A)
0	0
0.2	0.013
0.4	0.027
0.6	0.040
0.8	0.053
1.0	0.067

a) On the graph paper, plot a graph of V (horizontal axis) against I (vertical axis). *(4 marks)*

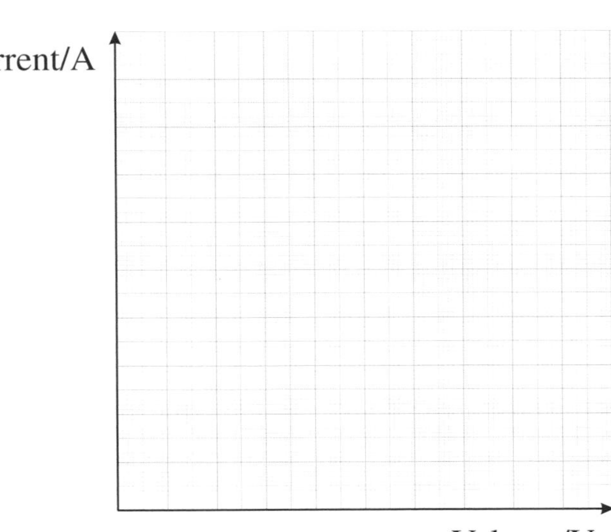

b) What SI units would you use to measure V and I?

i) V? .... *(1 mark)*

ii) I? .... *(1 mark)*

c) From the shape of the curve, decide which component R is likely to be.

.... *(1 mark)*

5) Which of the following hazard signs, A, B, C or D is used to indicate the presence of a radioactivity hazard?

A 

B 

C 

D 

Sign ....

6) Kate's elder brother has just got married and has moved into a new home. He and his wife want to work out how much they are spending on electricity. When they moved into the house on September 1st, they wrote down the reading on their electricity meter:

4 9 6 3 9 8 5 . 3 units

They read the meter again on December 1st. This time it reads

4 9 6 4 7 3 9 . 6 units

a) What *scientific* unit do we give for the term "unit"?

....

(1 mark)

b) Calculate the number of units used.

....

....

(1 mark)

c) If electricity costs 6.3p per unit, calculate the cost of the electricity used.

....

....

(1 mark)

d) There is also a fixed standing charge of £7.50. What will the total bill be, excluding VAT?

....

(1 mark)

e) State, with a reason, whether you would expect the bill to be higher or lower for the period

i) December 1st to March 1st ....

Reason ....

(2 marks)

ii) June 1st to September 1st ....

Reason ....

(2 marks)

7) This graph shows how the speed of a remote controlled car varies with time.

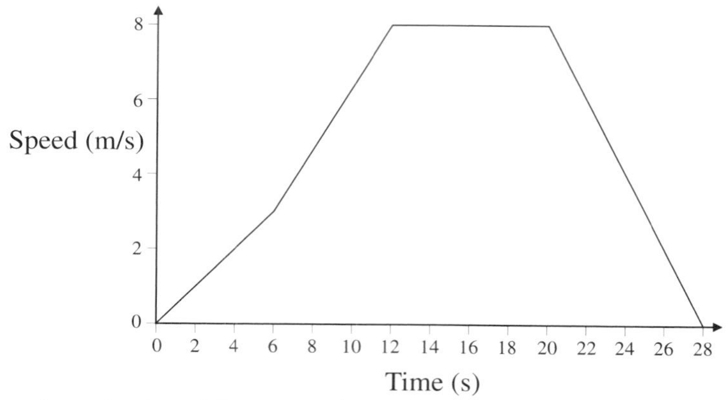

a) The speed of the car is not the same as the velocity. What else do we need to know about the car's motion to find its velocity at a particular time?

....

(1 mark)

Leave margin blank

b) If the maximum speed shown in the graph is the top speed for the car what is the best possible time that could be achieved for one circuit of a track 96m long?

....

....
(2 mark)

c) Imagine you were designing the track in question b. Name a feature you could put in to make it impossible to achieve the time you calculated and describe its effect on the car.

....

....
(2 mark)

d) During which period is the magnitude of acceleration least?

....

....
(1 mark)

e) Use values read from the graph for speed at time = 0s and time = 6s to calculate the acceleration during the first 6 seconds?

....

....
(3 mark)

8) A circuit is set up to measure the resistance of a certain component, R

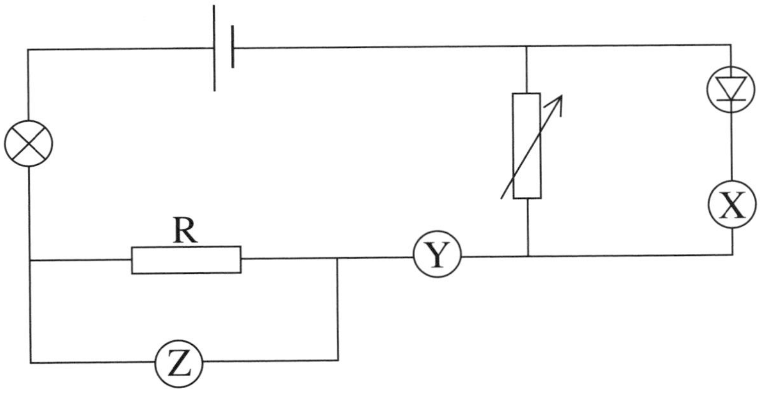

R

Y

X

Z

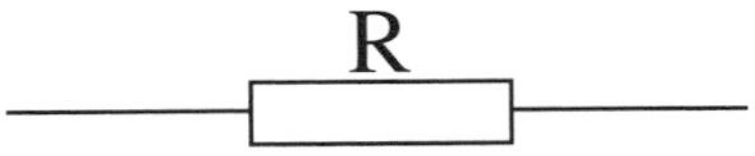

a) If you were setting up the circuit, which positions, X, Y, Z, would you choose to insert the ammeter and voltmeter?

i) Ammeter? ....
(1 mark)

ii) Voltmeter? ....
(1 mark)

b) What scientific term is used to describe the arrangement of

i) The variable resistor and diode? ....
(1 mark)

ii) The variable resistor, component R and the lamp? ....
(1 mark)

9) A group of astronomers are studying a group of stars, and have taken a photograph using the Hubble Space Telescope.

a) What is the name given to fixed patterns of stars?

....

(1 mark)

b) Give two advantages of having the telescope in orbit around the Earth.

Advantage 1...

Advantage 2 ....

(2 marks)

The astronomers use special instruments to study the light given off from the stars. They split the light up, and then they can identify the elements present in the star.

c) Name something that can be used to split light up into different colours.

....

(1 mark)

d) What is the name of the process that stars use to generate their energy?

....

(1 mark)

10) The diagram below shows a ray of light travelling from one medium into another.

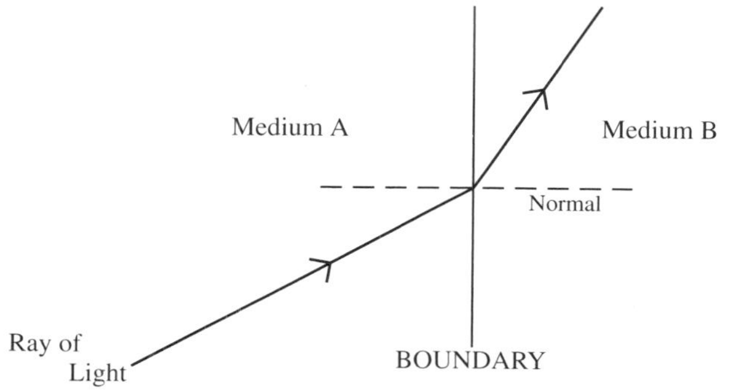

Medium A

Medium B

Normal

Ray of Light

BOUNDARY

a) On the diagram, mark the angle of incidence (i) and the angle of refraction (r).

(2 marks)

b) When the light travels from medium **A** to medium **B**, does its speed increase or decrease?

....

(1 mark)

c) How can you tell from the diagram that the change you indicated in b has happened?

....

....

(2 marks)

d) What do we call the process by which the direction of light changes when it goes from one medium to another?

....

(1 mark)

11) Some medical physicists are planning to use a radioactive isotope as a tracer inside the body of a patient. The isotope that they have decided to use is iodine, $^{131}_{53}I$.

a) In an atom of this isotope, how many protons and neutrons are there?

i) Protons ....

ii) Neutrons ....

(2 marks)

b) What are the beta particles that are given off when the iodine decays?

....

(1 mark)

c) Why is a beta emitter more suitable for this use than an alpha emitter?

....

....

(2 marks)

d) Give the name of the device that they could use to detect the radiation.

....

(1 mark)

e) Give three sources of background radiation.

....

....

....

(3 marks)

For another part of their work, they are asked to prepare a radioactive sample that can be used to treat a cancerous growth in one lung of a patient.

f) What type of radiation would you recommend for this use? Give reasons for your choice.

....

....

....

(3 marks)

g) Is treatment of this sort totally safe for the patient?

....

(1 mark)

h) List 3 safety precautions that the physicists might take whilst carrying out the treatment.

....

....

....

(3 marks)

12) The table below gives some information about our Solar system.

	Mass (Earth masses)	Distance from Sun (millions of km)	Weight of 1kg at surface (newtons)
Sun	333 000	—	270
Mercury	0.06	58	4
Venus	0.82	110	9
Earth	1	150	10
Moon	0.013	150	1.6
Mars	0.11	228	4
Jupiter	318	780	26
Saturn	95	1430	11

a) Which *planet* in the table has the greatest mass?

....

(1 mark)

b) Which object in the table is a star?

....

(1 mark)

c) Which planet has the orbit closest to the Earth's?

....

(1 mark)

d) On the surface of which two planets would you have the same weight?

....

(1 mark)

13) The diagram below shows what happens when white light travels through a prism. The light is dispersed, giving a range of colours.

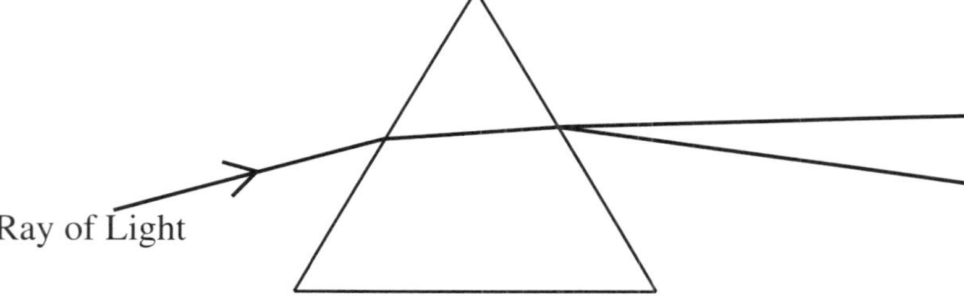

a) What do we call the range of colours produced in this way?

....

(1 mark)

b) The diagram shows the position of the range of the colours. On the diagram, mark the positions of red (R) and violet (V). *(1 mark)*

Leave margin blank

14) A spring has a unstretched length of 20mm. An experiment is carried out in which loads are attached to the spring and its extension measured.

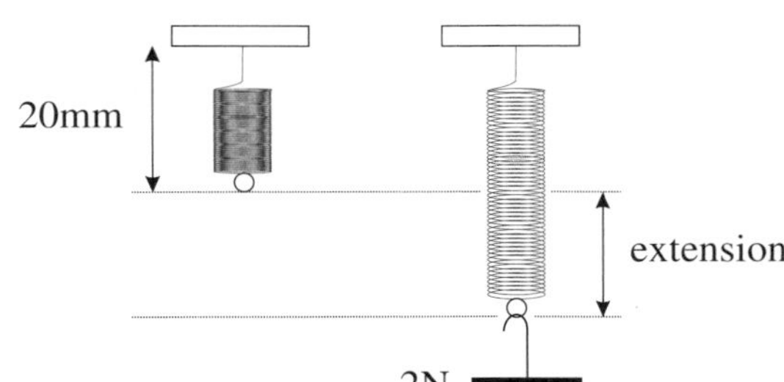

The results are shown in the table.

Load/ N	Extension/ mm
0	0
2	5
4	10
6	15
8	20
10	40

a) Plot the results on the axes and draw a best fit line through the points. *(2 marks)*

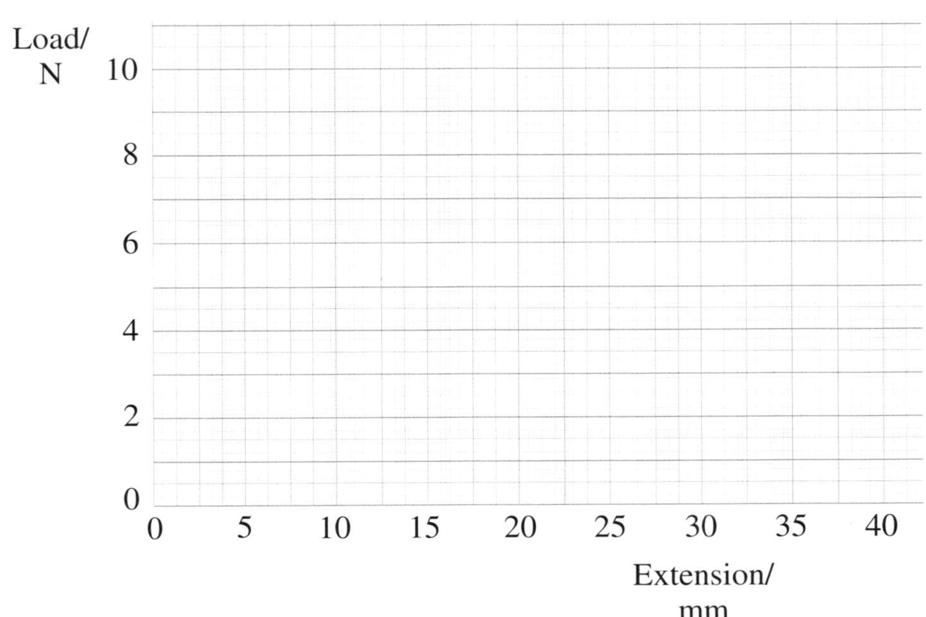

b) What is the extension of the spring with a load of 7N attached?

....

(1 mark)

c) Describe what happens to the spring when its extension exceeds 20mm.

....

....

(2 marks)

15) A power station is being designed to burn natural gas fuel and generate electricity.

a) Natural gas is a non-renewable fuel. Give two disadvantages of using non-renewable fuels.

....

....

....

(2 marks)

b) Give the names of two other non-renewable fuels that you know.

....

....

(3 marks)

c) What sort of energy does the natural gas fuel have?

....

(1 mark)

The power station produces electrical energy.

d) Complete the energy flow diagram below showing the basic features of the power station, and show the energy types that are involved at each stage. *(4 marks)*

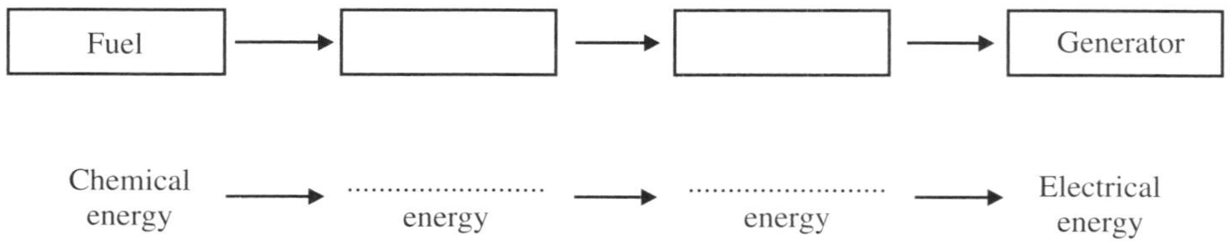

Fuel → [ ] → [ ] → Generator

Chemical energy → .... energy → .... energy → Electrical energy

Before the electricity is sent to the National Grid, the voltage is stepped up to 400kV.

e) Explain why this is done. Use the relationship between power, voltage and current in your answer.

....

....

....

....

(4 marks)

f) Give two reasons why the voltage is transformed back down to 240V before it comes into our houses.

(2 marks)

Reason 1 ....

Reason 2 ....

(2 marks)

16) The diagram opposite shows a coil of wire connected to a galvanometer. The north pole of a magnet is being held near the end of the coil.

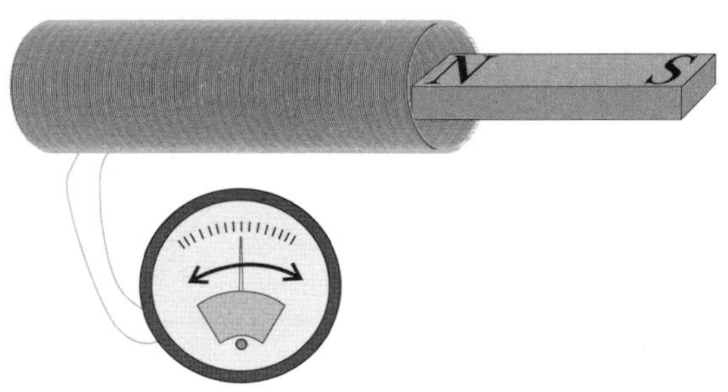

When the bar magnet is moved into the coil of wire, the needle on the galvanometer moves to the left, one division.

Complete the rest of the table showing the results of various experiments with the coil and bar magnet. *(5 marks)*

Pole of magnet	*Direction moved*	*Speed of movement*	*Galvonometer direction*	*How far?*
North	Into coil	Slowly	Left	1 div
North	Into coil	Quickly		
North	Out of coil	Slowly		
South	Into coil	Quickly		2 div

17) The diagram below shows a water wave travelling along a canal.

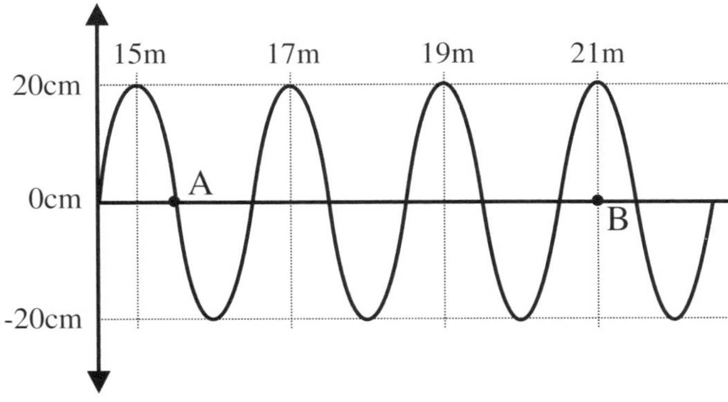

a) What is the wavelength of the wave?

....

(1 mark)

The wave takes 2 seconds to travel from point A to point B.

b) Calculate the speed of the wave.

....

....

....

(2 marks)

18) A pupil uses an oscilloscope to display the wave pattern of a musical note. The pattern he sees on the screen is shown below.

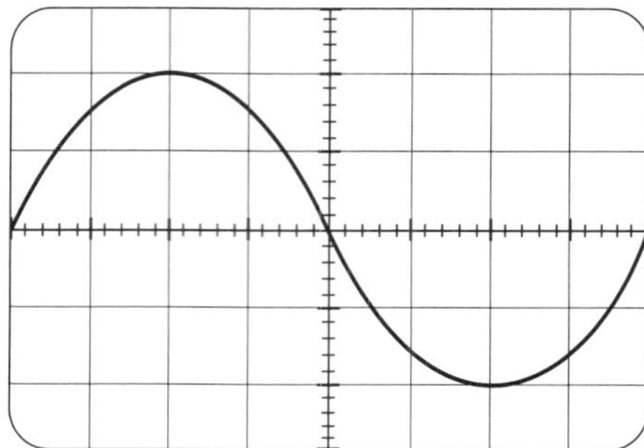

The pupil changes the note without changing any of the controls on the oscilloscope.

a) Draw the pattern he would get if the sound is quieter than the first, but with the same frequency.

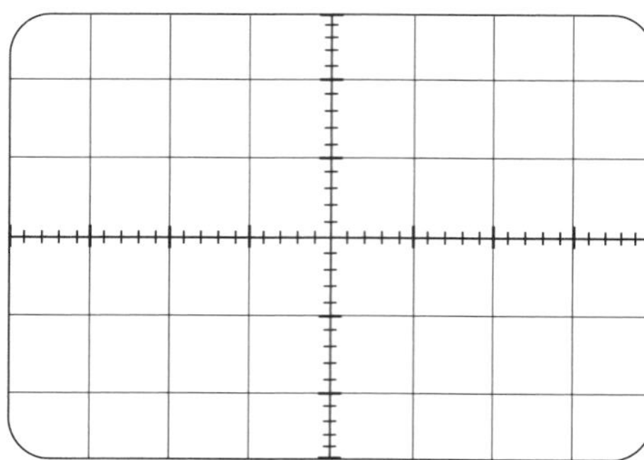

(2 marks)

b) Draw the pattern he would obtain if he used a note of the same loudness as the first, but with a higher frequency.

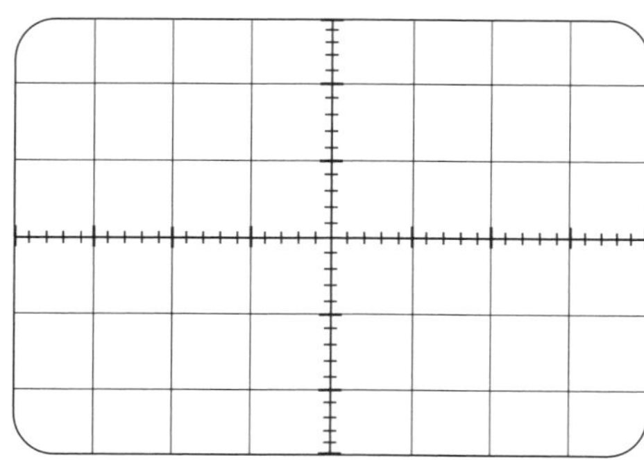

(2 marks)

c) The pupil increases the frequency of the note until he can not hear it anymore.

i) What name is given to sounds beyond the range of human hearing?

....

(1 mark)

ii) Give two uses of this type of sound: one use by humans and one by an animal.

Humans ....

Animal ....

(2 marks)